page 35

20 10 30 40 50

page 36

8 7 5 6 9

page 38

1p 5p 2p 20p 10p £1 50p £2

page 40

page 41

page 46

3rd 6th

7th 9th

page 49

page 54

page 60

page 63

page 3

page 6

page 15

pages 30–31

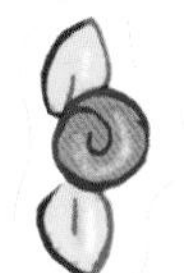

page 73
page 75
page 87
pages 88–89
page 93
page 94

page 98

52 81 24 35

page 100

30 25 40

page 107

page 108

page 110

game 1

Adam	Chloe	Ellie
76	62	81
Ben	**David**	**Frankie**
45	58	73

game 2

Adam	Chloe	Ellie
77	42	35
Ben	**David**	**Frankie**
79	50	93

page 113

page 115

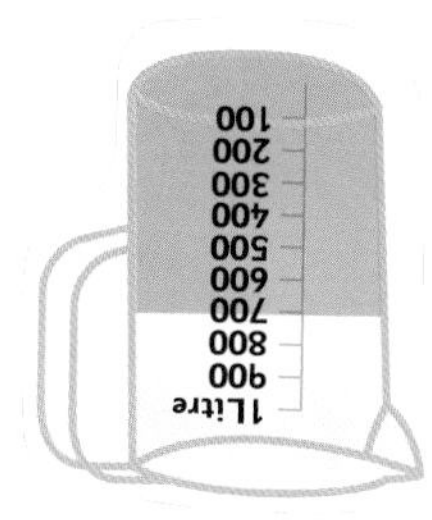

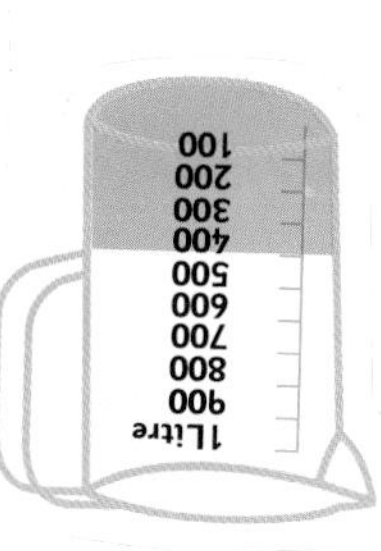

page 117

Well done!

page 118

6 60 14 18 12 30

15 25 50 40 35 10

page 120

page 122

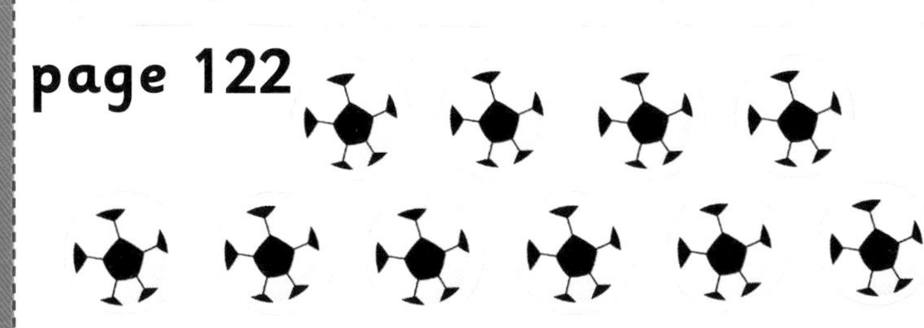

page 125

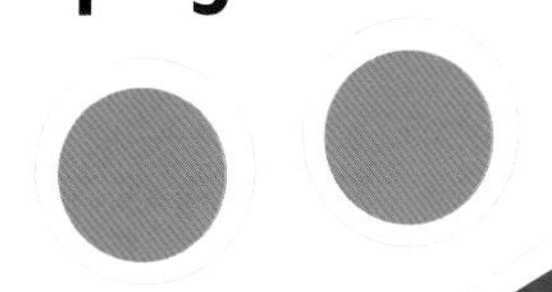

page 125

page 126

5-6 years

Leap Ahead

BUMPER Workbook

ENGLISH

Home learning made FUN!

igloobooks

About Me

Read the instructions and draw a picture in each box.

This is me:

This is my family:

This is my home:

Sticker Match

Read each word out loud. Then, find the matching sticker. The first two have been done for you.

dog 

pin 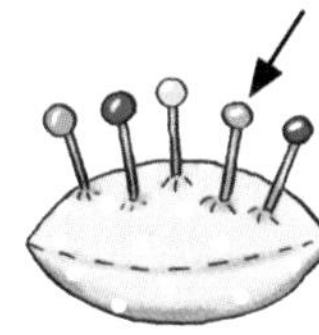

can 

map 

ten 

hat 

hen 

sun 

bed 

bib 

rock 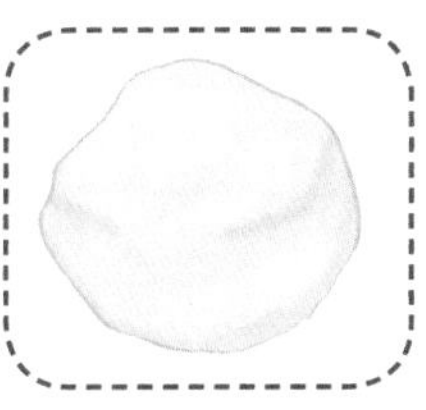

sack 

chip 

bath 

PARENT TIP: These words are all 'decodable'. In other words, they are said how they are spelt. In phonics lessons, children learn to 'sound-talk' these words by saying each sound individually, e.g. 't-e-n'.

The Witch's Washing

Find the letters of the alphabet floating in the cauldron and write them in the correct order on the witch's washing line. Some have been done for you.

PARENT TIP: Although your child will recognise most letters by now, it is useful for them to remember what order they come in so that they can start to use dictionaries and indexes.

a
c
i
q
v

Two Letters, One Sound

Use the correct letter pairs to complete the words below. Then find the stickers of the missing pictures. Each letter pair may be used more than once. The first one has been done for you.

Answers on page 32

PARENT TIP: A 'phoneme' is a single sound in a word. Sometimes it is made by one letter, e.g. the 'p' in 'pot', and sometimes it is made by two or more letters, e.g. the 's' sound in 'fuss' or the 'th' in 'bath'.

Tricky Letters

Some words with tricky letters are hiding in the picture below. See if you can find them, then choose the correct letters from the box to complete each label.

qu	x	y	z

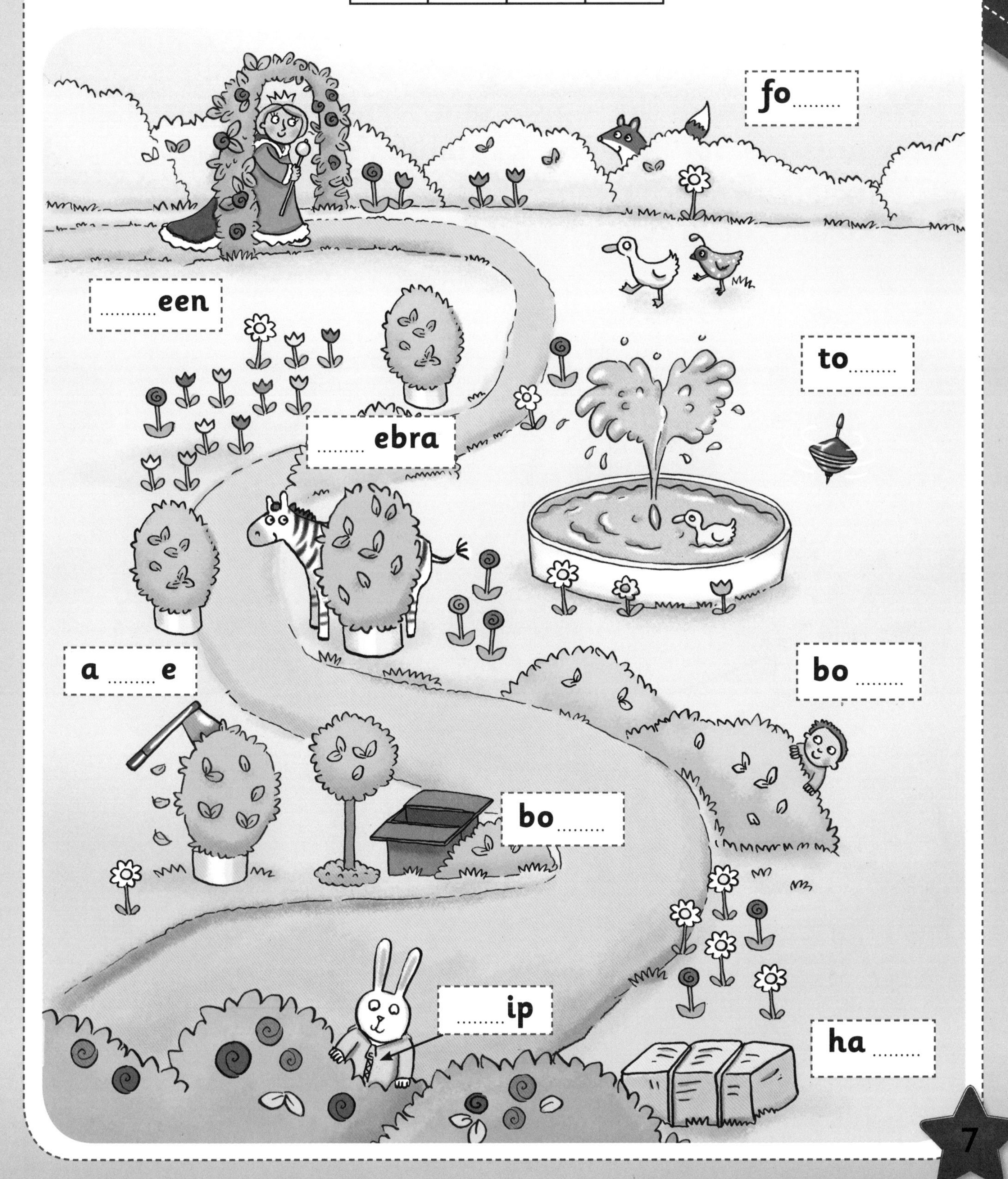

A Trip to the Zoo

Megan's class has been on a trip to the zoo. Read Megan's report. Then write numbers in the circles to show the order the class visited each place. The first one is done for you.

Our trip to the zoo

We started by the cafe. We walked towards the monkeys. Then, we turned left towards the giraffes. We went around the hippos and then turned right towards the gorillas. The last animals we saw were the elephants. Afterwards we had an ice cream at the ice cream van. Then we got on the bus and went home.

Answers on page 32

Robot Names

Rearrange the letters in these robot names to make words.
Draw a line to match each robot up to the correct word.
The first one has been done for you.

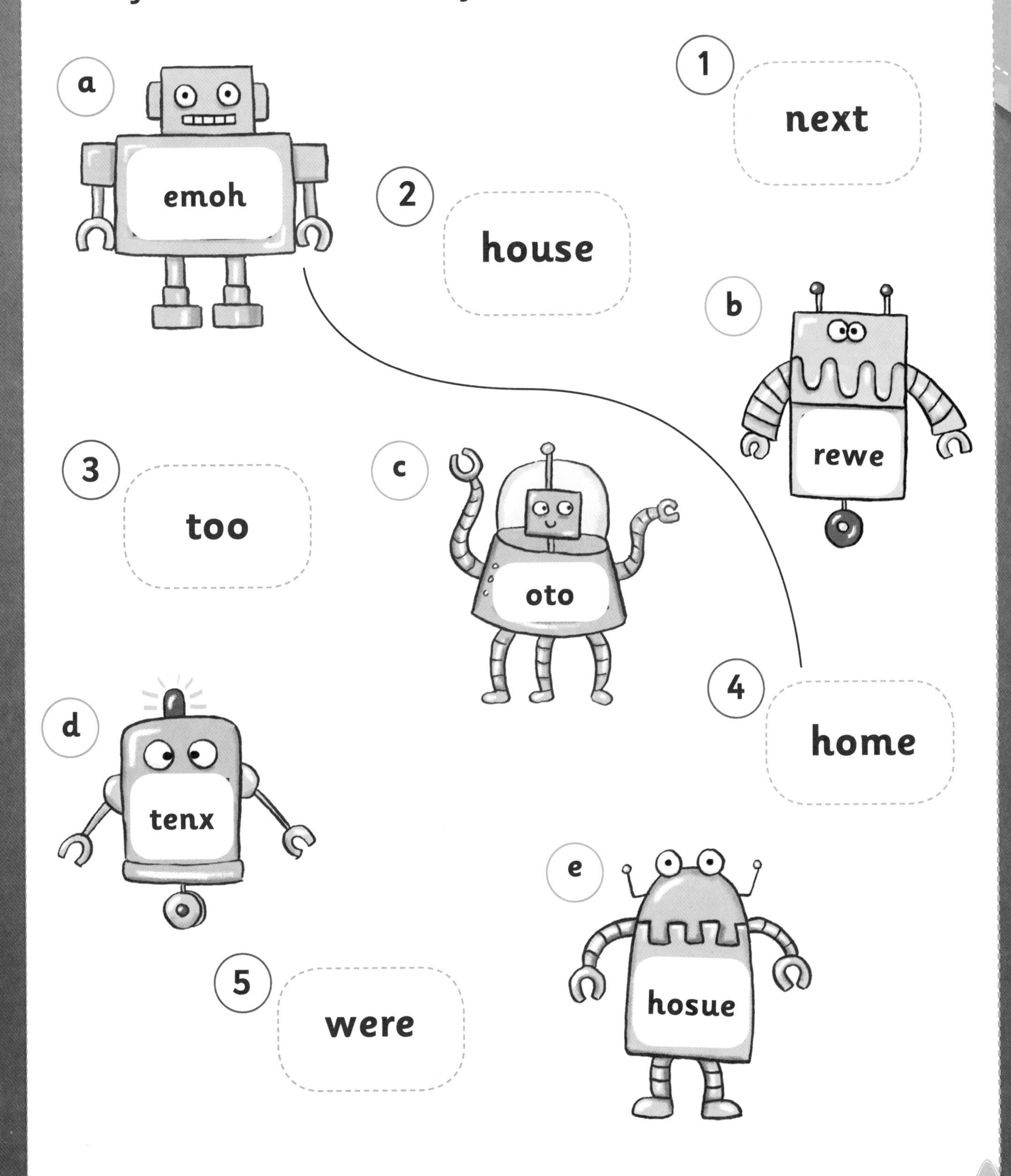

Answers on page 32

Magic Spellings

Some of the vowels have dropped out of the magician's spell book! Choose the correct vowels to complete the words. The five vowels are listed in the box below to help you.

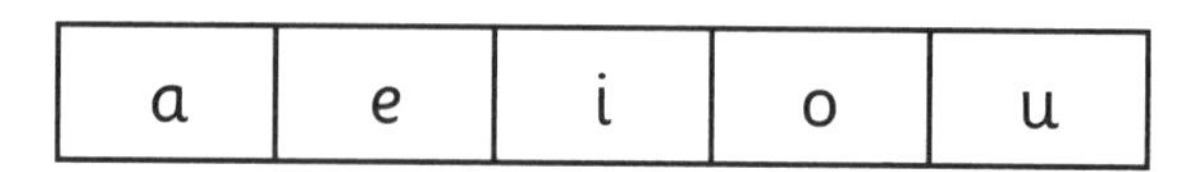

a	e	i	o	u

A spell to put a fr....... g in your sister's b....... th.

A s....... lly tr....... ck to play on your m....... m.

How to make a c....... t turn p....... nk.

These items are missing the last two letters in their names. Can you add either 'ng' or 'nk' in the correct places? The first one has been done for you.

sink

wi ....

si ....

i ....

PARENT TIP: Explain to your child that the letter 'y' sometimes sounds like a vowel, such as in the word 'sky', but because the sound it most often makes is the 'y' as in 'yellow', it isn't referred to as one.

Guess Who?

Read each description, then look at the pictures.
Draw lines to match each description to the right person.

a This person has not got black hair. He has a red hat. He has a blue jumper and he has got a book in his hands. His name is Tom.

b This girl has got a pink dress. She has a teddy in a red bag. Her name is Becky.

2

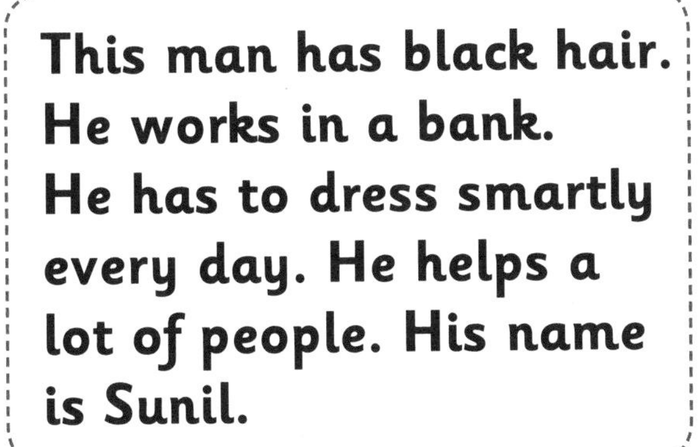
c This man has black hair. He works in a bank. He has to dress smartly every day. He helps a lot of people. His name is Sunil.

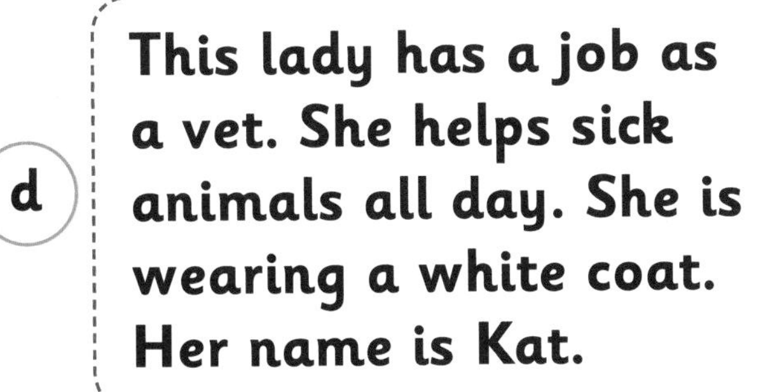
d This lady has a job as a vet. She helps sick animals all day. She is wearing a white coat. Her name is Kat.

Answers on page 32

Busy Toyshop

Can you spot all of the things in the box on the right in the toyshop? When you find them, list each word under the correct spelling pattern. The first ones have been done for you.

ai	oa	ee
rail	coat	feet
....	....	....
....	....	....
....	....	....
....	....	....
....	....	....
....	....	....

feet, teeth, boat, coat, jeep, train, rain, stain, goat, free, throat, cheese, tree, road, toad, foal, week, sail, tail, rail, sweet

PARENT TIP: A 'digraph' is one sound that is made by two letters. Each of the words in this activity contains a common vowel digraph. Learning to recognise these digraphs without sounding out each letter will help your child to read new words.

Missing Letters

Add the missing letters to these words that you found on the previous page. The first one has been done for you.

feet	c .... t	g .... t
t .... th	tr .... n	s l
t .... d	st .... n	sw .... t

Can you write some short sentences using some of the words above?

1. I have big feet and little hands.

2. ....

....

3. ....

....

4. ....

....

5. ....

....

6. ....

....

7. ....

....

Party Time!

Write the missing capital letters beneath the lower case letters to fill in the spaces on the bunting. Then, decorate the page with party stickers from your sticker sheet.

Me First

Look at each of these pictures and complete the missing words using the letters in the box. Which nouns need a capital letter?

~~c~~	J	F	t	S	b

cup .... **ree** .... **ally**

.... **ack** .... **ido** .... **ox**

Sentences always start with a capital letter. Which of the following are sentences? Fill in the missing letters, using capital letters at the start of any full sentences.

1. ....**y dad's dog is called Fido.**

2. ....**potty dog**

3. ....**y family**

4. ....**his is my car.**

Answers on page 32

PARENT TIP: Explain to your child that a noun is another name for an object or thing. A common noun is an everyday object and proper nouns describe just one thing or person. Proper nouns, e.g. people's names, always begin with a capital letter.

Stop at the Red Light

A full stop is the mark that we use to show that a sentence has finished. Read the story below. Add any full stops that you think are missing.

Mac is as fast as any car in town. He is as speedy as a train

Mac wants a race He asks Bus Bus says yes.

Mac and Bus are at the start The flag waves, "Go!"

Mac is fast Bus is last, but at the end of the street the lights are red

The lights are broken. No one can go

The broken light means they both win.

Answers on page 32

Adding Apostrophes

Match each of these words with apostrophes below to its long version.

I'll	We will
He'll	I will
We'll	He will
They'll	She will
She'll	They will

Choose which word from the box should go in each sentence.

I'll	she'll	we'll	he'll

If we don't hurry up, ... be late.

I am going out now, but .... see you later.

When Mum comes, ... give us our lunch.

Uncle Fred has funny hats. Which one do you think .... be wearing today?

Answers on page 32

Circus Syllables

Syllables are like beats within words, e.g. ti–ger. Read these words out loud and write dots underneath to show how many syllables are in each word. The first one has been done for you.

Answers on page 32

Time for a Puzzle

Which letters from the box are missing from the clues below? Write each word that you complete in the crossword. One has been done for you.

or	ar	oo

						1			
				2					
			3 l	o	o	k			
							4		
			5						
					6				
7									

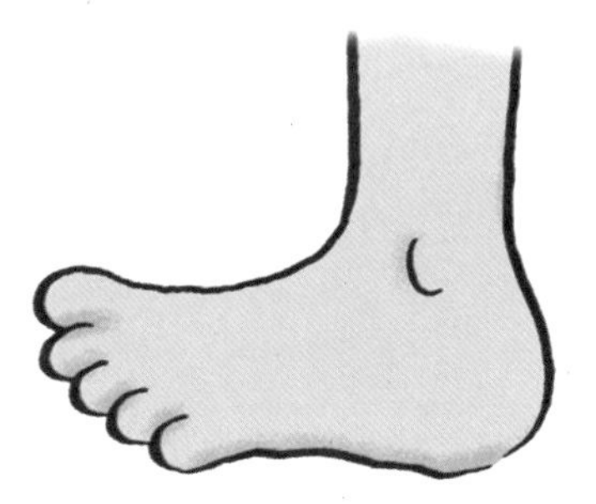

Across

1. The b _ _ n is red.
3. Look over there!
5. It's time to st _ _ t work.
6. It is too f _ _ to run.
7. I hurt my f _ _ t on the beach.

Down

1. Can you find my b _ _ k?
2. This dress is too sh _ _ t.
4. It is a shiny st _ _.
5. Is it the right s _ _ t of cheese?
6. Is this f _ _ me?

Answers on page 32

Remember, Remember

Read these words and try to remember how they are spelt. Write them on a separate piece of paper. How did you do?

going	began	think	things
food	fast	again	bear
wanted	these	first	boy
other	play	thought	magic
shouted	long	where	would
never	cried	before	night
mouse	boy	been	door
much	good	small	found
there	some	down	back
asked	can't	said	they

PARENT TIP: If you have not tried it with your child before, a good method of learning spellings is to 'read, cover, write, check'. First, have them read the word, then cover it and try to write it from memory. When they have finished, look back to see if they were right.

I Spy Spellings

Play I Spy in this fun beach scene, using the phonemes in the boxes below. For example, "I spy with my little eye, something with an 'air' sound." Take it in turns to ask and answer. When you find each item, write it under the correct phoneme at the bottom.

You should be able to find all of these items.
What else can you spot?

chair, coat, tears, summer, spear, soap, butter, tart, cheese, mother, start, pair, father, sneeze, star, boat, cart, feet, sheet, hammer

oa	**er**	**ear**
....	....	....
....	....	....
....	....	....
....	....	....
....	....	....

Consonant or Vowel?

Follow the key and colour the grid. What picture can you see when all the squares are coloured?

vowel = 

consonant = 

q	w	r	t	y	p	s	d	f	g	h	j
d	s	z	x	c	v	b	n	i	m	l	k
f	g	h	j	k	l	p	y	o	t	r	w
h	g	k	l	p	y	t	r	a	i	w	q
f	d	s	q	w	r	t	y	o	o	p	y
q	a	e	i	u	i	a	u	u	e	i	t
w	a	o	u	o	e	i	o	e	a	o	r
r	m	n	b	v	c	x	q	o	e	s	d
t	y	p	y	t	r	w	q	e	u	z	x
f	g	h	j	k	l	m	n	a	b	v	c
d	s	q	w	r	t	y	p	i	l	j	h
f	l	k	h	v	m	b	b	c	d	f	g

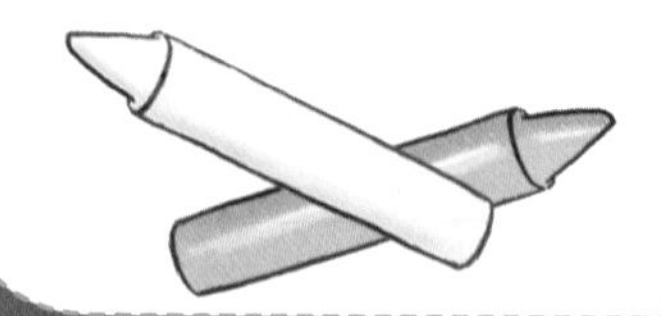

Answer on page 32

PARENT TIP: Explain to your child that vowels are the letters 'a', 'e', 'i', 'o' and 'u'. All the other letters of the alphabet are consonants.

Word Score

Use a separate piece of paper to play this word game. Make words by picking two consonant letter tiles and one vowel combination. Add up the points on each tile to make a score for each word. What's your highest scoring word?

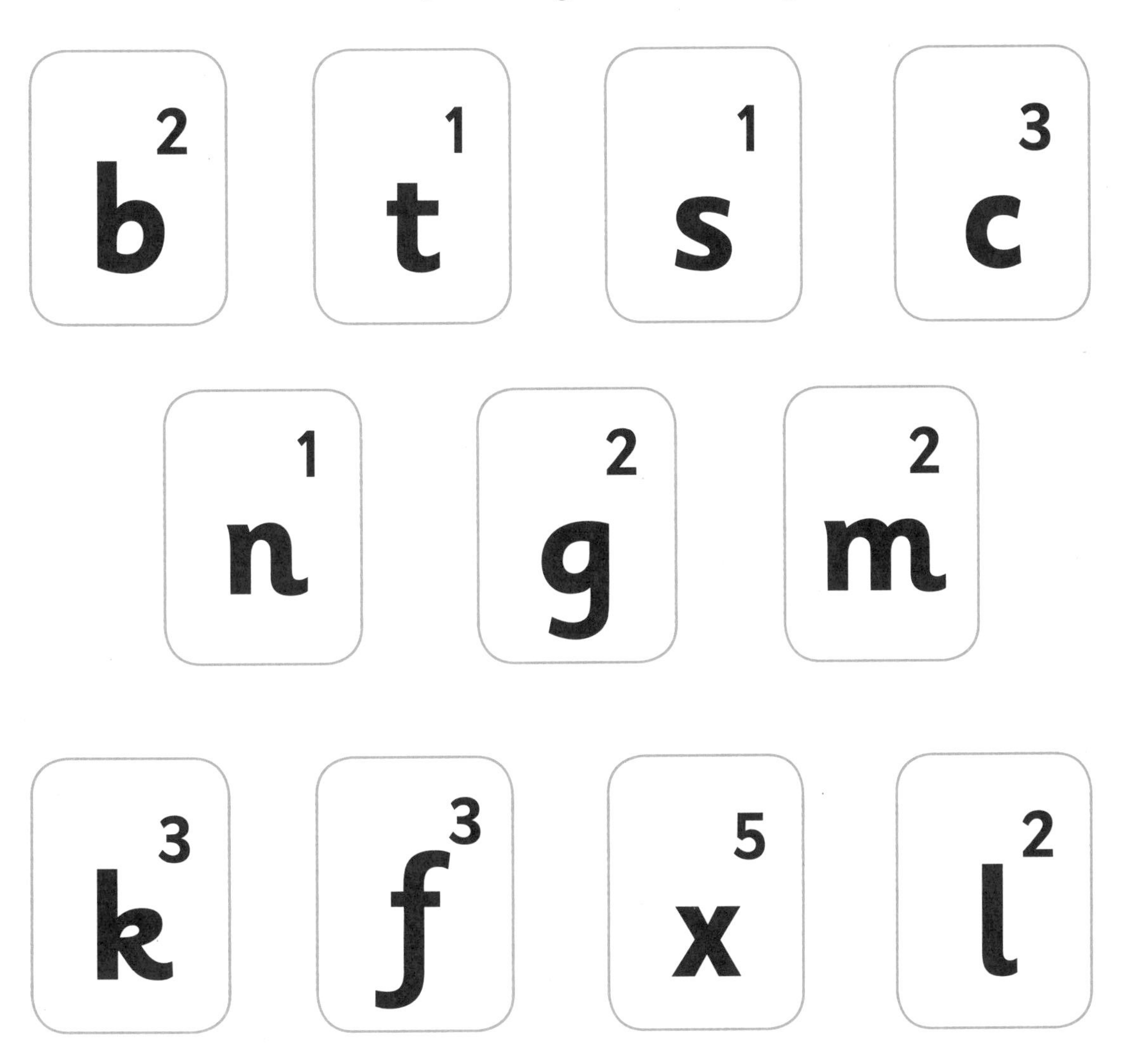

Example: b u t = 3 points, f ee t = 4 points, b o x = 7 points

o | ee | oa | u | oo | ar

Punctuation

Not all sentences end in full stops. Some use question marks or exclamation marks.

Look at these examples:

Would you like a drink?

Don't look!

Now add the correct punctuation to the end of these sentences.

1. Do you have a hat ....
2. Can I have a sandwich ....
3. No ....
4. What do you want ....
5. It's a trick ....
6. What a mess ....
7. How does it work ....
8. Is it his or hers ....

Answers on page 32

If I Was a Pirate...

If you were a pirate, what would your pirate name be?

Pirate name ....

Who would your shipmates be?

My shipmates ....

....

What would your ship be called?

The Good Ship ....

Where would you go for your first pirate adventure?

....

....

What would happen?

....

....

....

....

....

....

PARENT TIP: Make-believe is a great way to develop children's creativity and vocabulary, too. Talk about your child's ideas and let them grow!

Be the Author

Look at the pictures below and write a sentence under each picture to make a story. Draw the last picture yourself and make up the ending.

The Escape

1

Jess the cat was fed up. She decided to run away.

2

3

4

5

6

7

8

Help the Farmer

Farmer Brown wants to rearrange his farm. Help him by using the words in the box to label each area. Use stickers from the sticker sheet to finish the farm.

sheep, cows, goats, ~~farm~~, barn, farmer's house, pigs, horses, hens, geese, ducks, tractor, shed, pond

Answers

Page 6: Two Letters, One Sound
buzz, bath, kiss, bell, cash, bull, shop, path, ship, sock.

Page 8: A Trip to the Zoo

Page 9: Robot Names
a – 4, b – 5, c – 3, d – 1, e – 2

Page 11: Guess Who?
a – 3, b – 4, c – 1, d – 2

Page 16: Me First
cup, tree, Sally, Jack, Fido, box.
Sally, Jack and Fido need capital letters.
My dad has a dog called Fido. – spotty dog – my family – This is my car.

Page 17: Stop at the Red Light
Mac is as fast as any car in town.
He is as speedy as a train.
Mac wants a race. He asks Bus.
Bus says yes.
Mac and Bus are at the start.
The flag waves, "Go!"
Mac is fast. Bus is last, but at the end of the street the lights are red.
The lights are broken.
No one can go.
The broken light means they both win.

Page 18: Adding Apostrophes
I'll – I will, He'll – He will, We'll – We will, They'll – They will, She'll – She will.
(The following answers may vary) If we don't hurry up, we'll be late. I am going out now, but I'll see you later. When Mum comes, she'll give us our lunch. Uncle Fred has funny hats. Which one do you think he'll be wearing today?

Page 19: Circus Syllables

Page 20: Time for a Puzzle

						1 b	a	r	n
				2 s		o			
				h		o			
			3 l	o	o	k			
				r			4 s		
			5 s	t	a	r	t		
			o				a		
			r		6 f	a	r		
7 f	o	o	t		o				
					r				

Page 24: Consonant or Vowel?
An arrow.

Page 26: Punctuation
Do you have a hat? Can I have a sandwich? No! What do you want? It's a trick! What a mess! How does it work? Is it his or hers?

Home learning made FUN!

Counting to 20

Look at all of these leopards. Estimate how many spots they have, then count the spots to see if you were right.

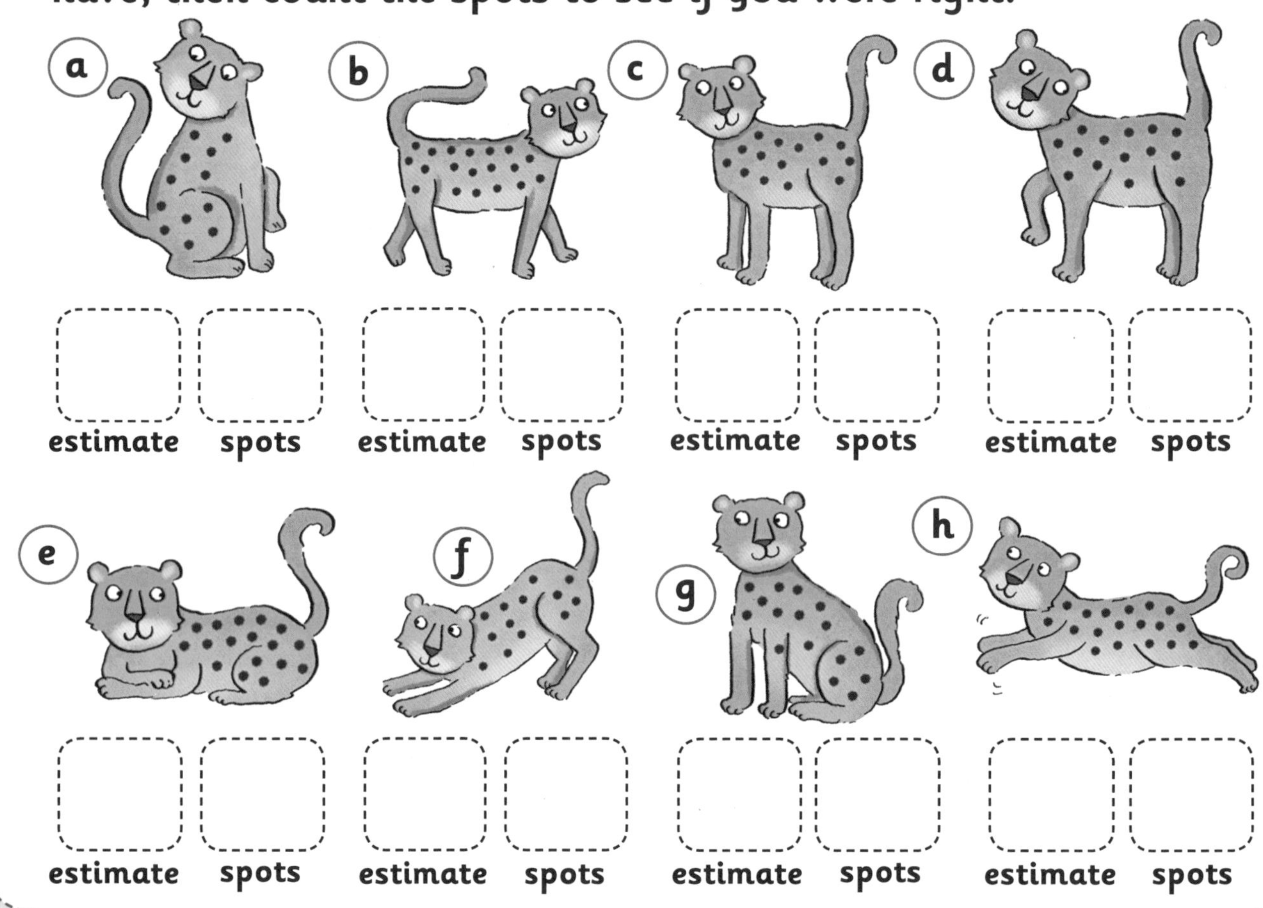

How many bugs are in this tank?

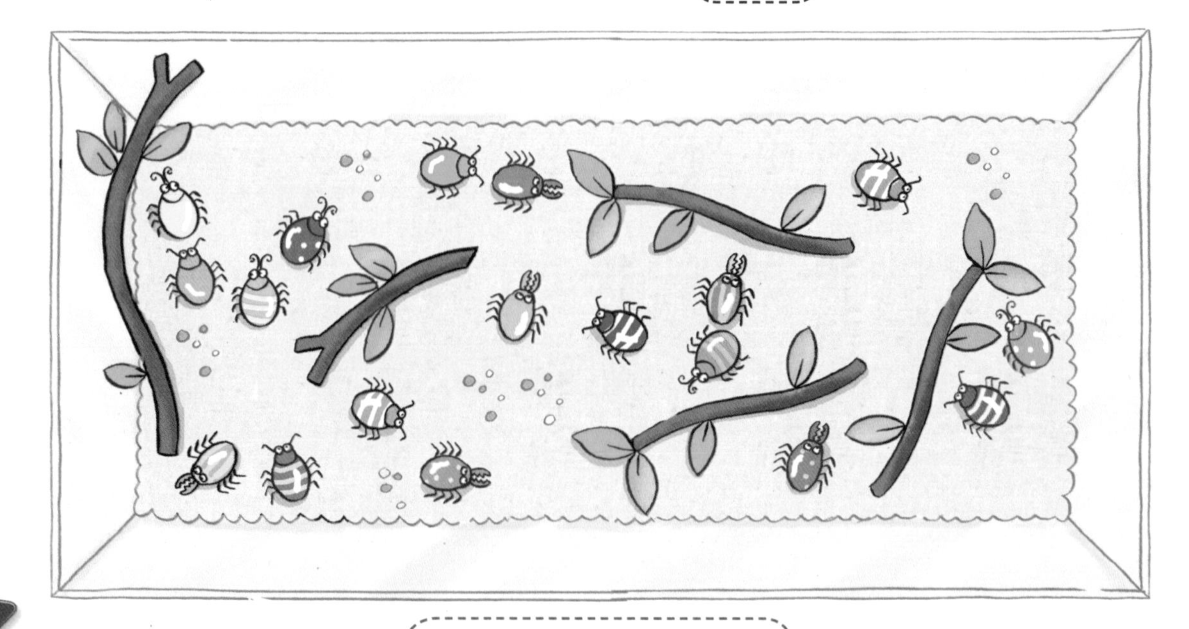

Answers on page 64

Teen Numbers and Words

Join each mouse to the correct mouse hole.

Answers on page 64

Find birthday card stickers that match these number words.

ten twenty thirty forty fifty

PARENT TIP: Children should be able to count consistently to 20 and beyond. Make sure they say the numbers and point to each object being counted. Also practise counting things that cannot be touched, such as footsteps, jumps and claps, as well as objects out of reach.

Make 10

Find the correct butterfly sticker to complete each butterfly. The numbers on both wings must add up to 10.

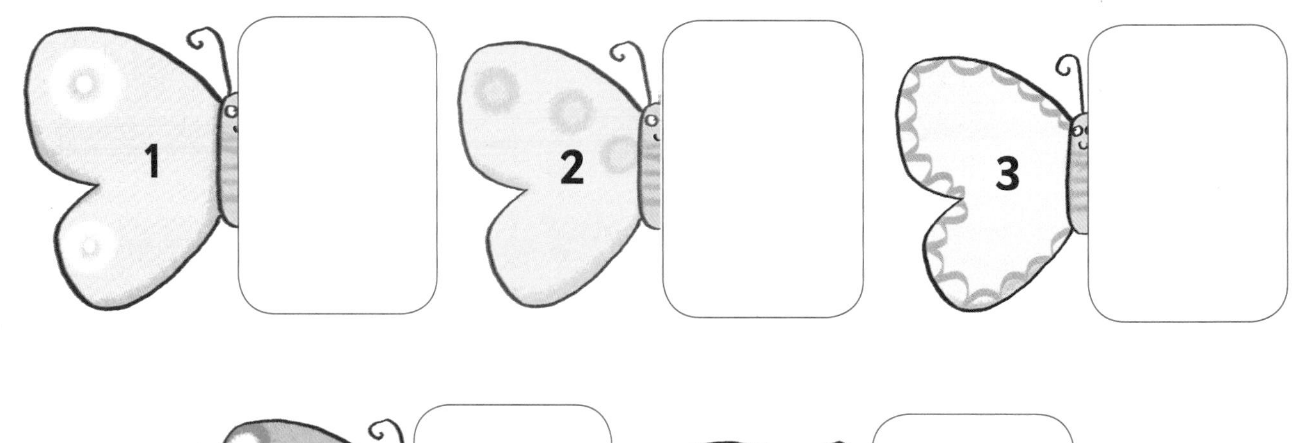

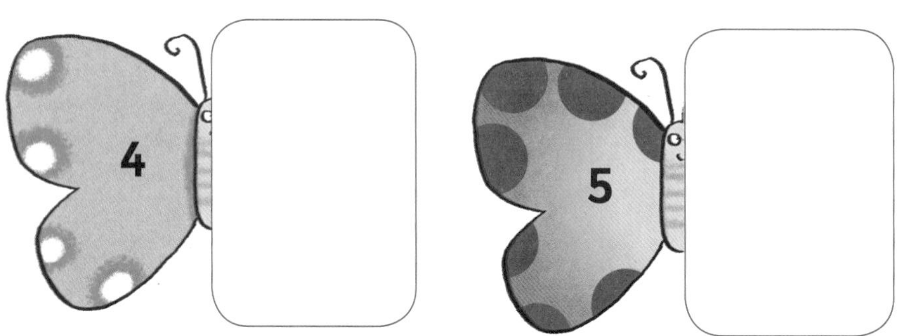

Complete these number sums.

a	1 + ☐ = 10		f	9 + ☐ = 10
b	2 + ☐ = 10		g	8 + ☐ = 10
c	3 + ☐ = 10		h	7 + ☐ = 10
d	4 + ☐ = 10		i	6 + ☐ = 10
e	5 + ☐ = 10		j	10 + ☐ = 10

Answers on page 64

Make 20

Choose pairs of beehives that have a total of 20 bees when added together. Join them with a line.

Answers on page 64

Colour pairs to make 20. Use different colours for each pair.

1	2	3	4	5	6	7	8	9
11	12	13	14	15	16	17	18	19

PARENT TIP: Knowing pairs that total 10 and using these to calculate pairs that total 20 is very important. Why not play a game? Say "4" and your child replies with the number to add to make 10. You could also play Number Pairs Snap. Have number cards to 20 and turn them over, looking for pairs that make 10 or 20.

Money Maths

Choose coin stickers to pay for these toys.

This goat costs 6p.
Tick the coins you could use to pay for it in each purse.

Count the money in each piggy bank.

Total = ☐ p   Total = ☐ p   Total = ☐ p

Answers on page 64

These things are for sale in the pet shop.
What is the cost of each basket of goods?

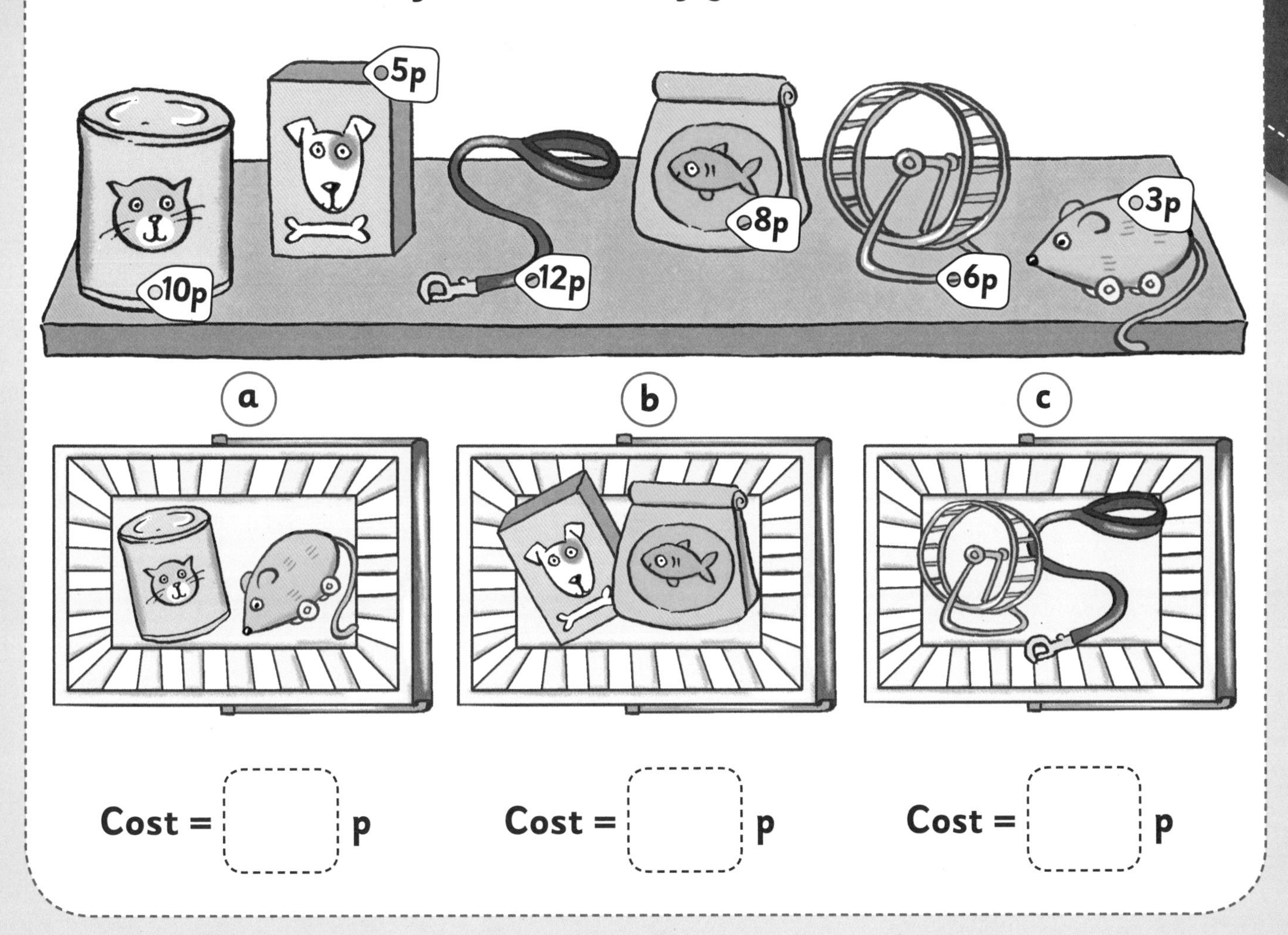

Cost = ☐ p

Cost = ☐ p

Cost = ☐ p

Rory buys a new dog lead. He has 20p.
How much change will he get?

Change = ☐ p

Carly buys some dog biscuits. She has 20p.
How much change will she get?

Change = ☐ p

Answers on page 64

PARENT TIP: Price up some food items from the cupboard at home and play Shops. Make the prices less than 20p, then buy each item one at a time and work out the change. When calculating change, get your child to count up from the price of the goods, e.g. if an apple is 14p, count up from 14p to 20p.

Missing Number Puzzles

These tanks have room for more ants. Count how many ants are already inside and work out how many extra can fit. Write the answers in the boxes.

a

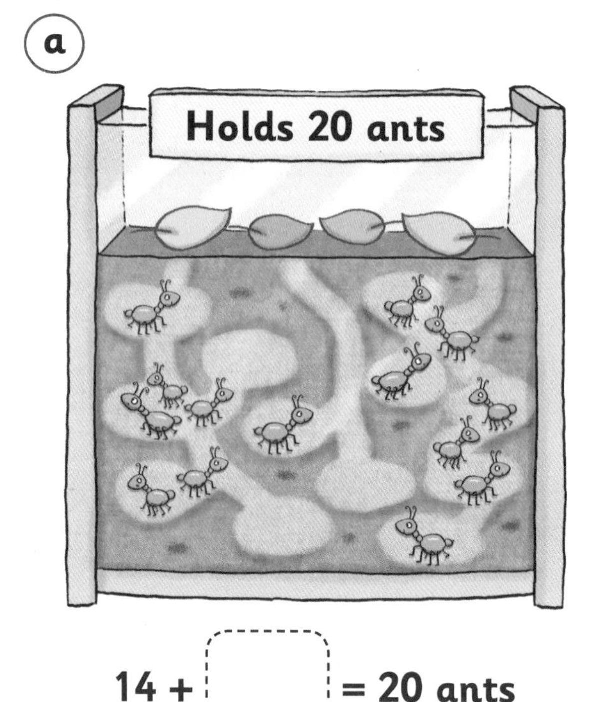

14 + ☐ = 20 ants

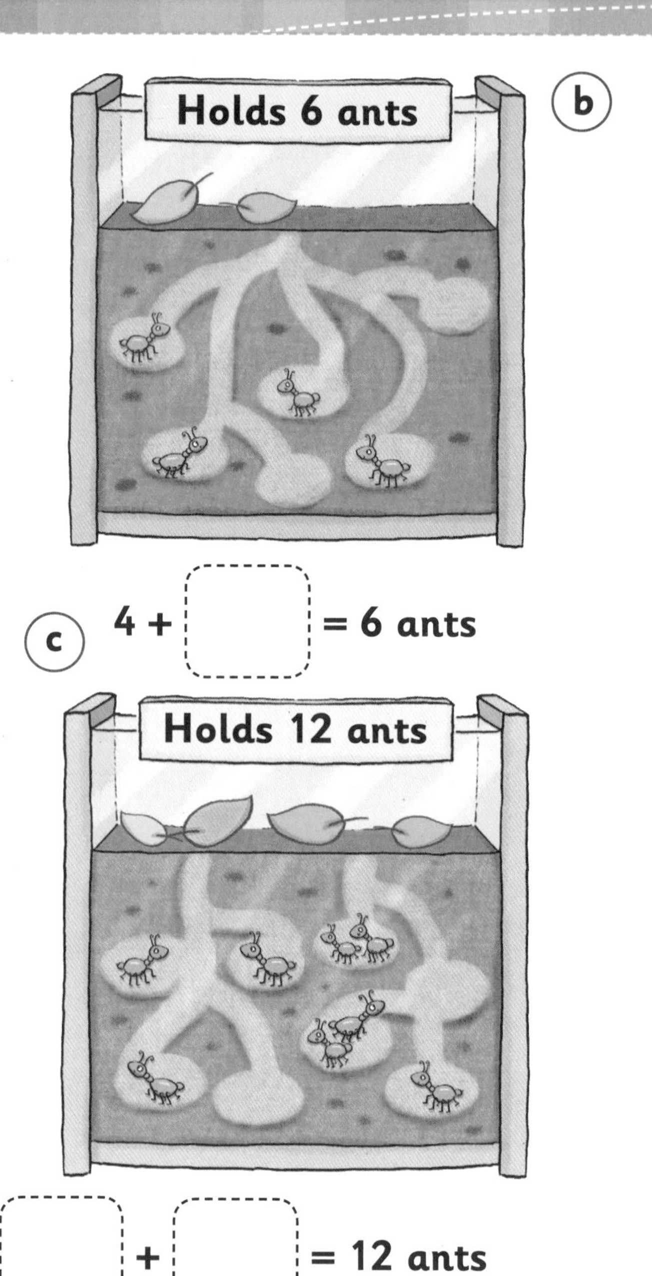

Find the ant stickers on the sticker sheet. Use the stickers to add more ants to the tank. How many do you need to make 20?

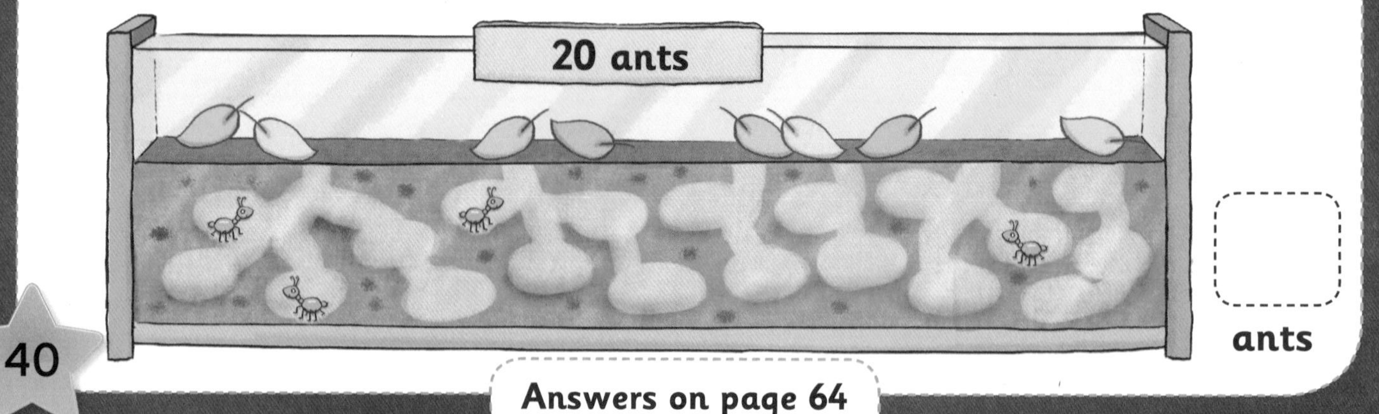

☐ ants

Answers on page 64

Repeating Patterns

Here are 3 snakes. Colour the patterns on their bodies. Each snake must look different.

These zoo animals have special identity numbers. Carry on the repeating number patterns.

Answers on page 64

Choose different coloured star stickers and make a repeating colour pattern.

PARENT TIP: Arrange toys and household objects into repeating patterns, such as spoon-fork-spoon-fork, on the dinner table. See if your child can describe the part of the pattern that repeats and then continue it themselves.

Counting On to Add

Help the monkeys cross the bridges. Count on from the start number to work out which number each monkey lands on.

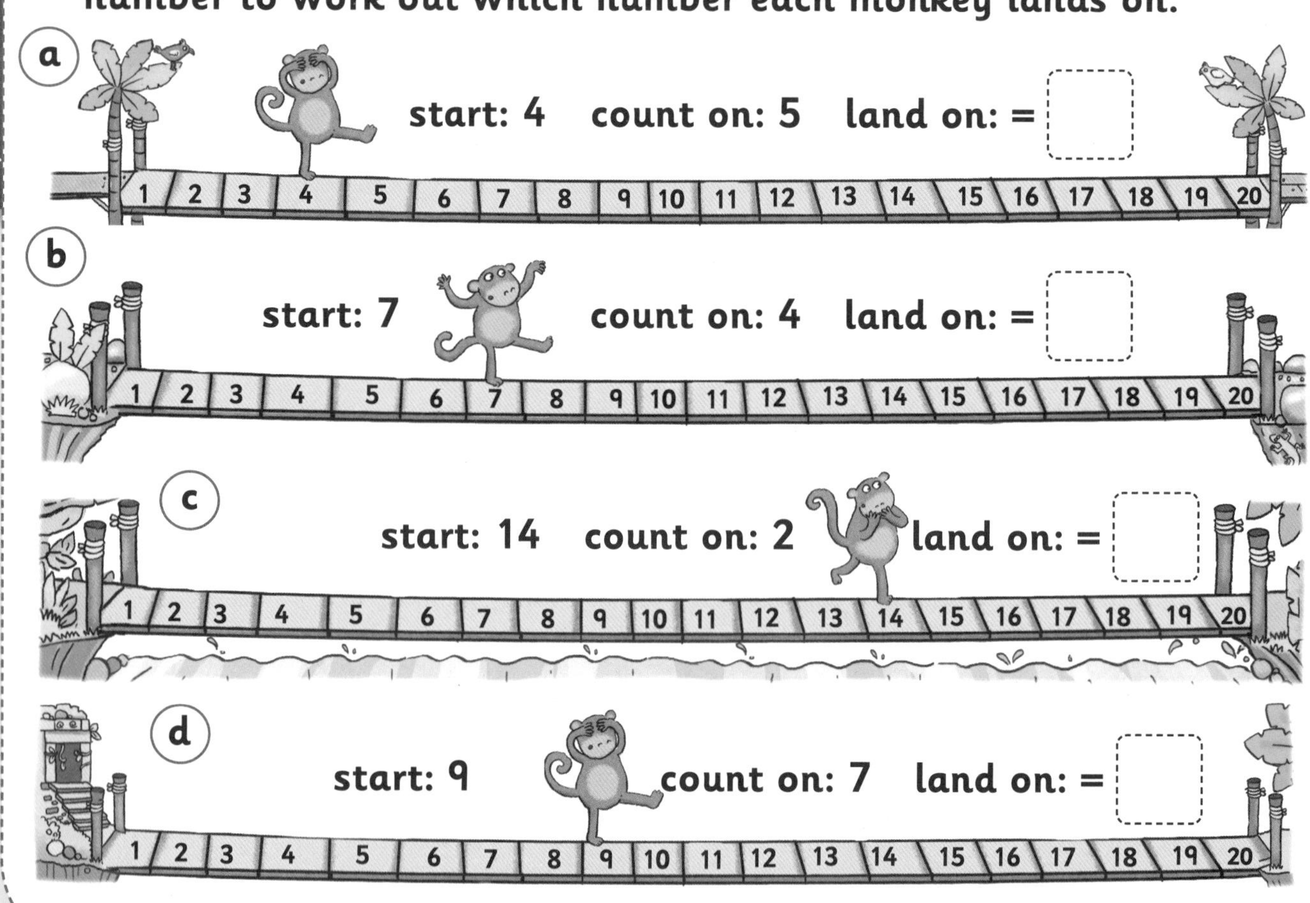

8 monkeys are already inside the party. Another 6 have arrived. How many does that make in total?

Answers on page 64

2D Shapes

Draw the other half of each shape. Match them to their names.

Star　　Square　　Triangle　　Circle

Draw 2 different 4-sided shapes.

Circle and count the points on this star.
How many sides does it have?

Points

Sides

Answers on page 64

PARENT TIP: Your child must learn to count on from different numbers when adding. Practise putting the largest number in your head, then counting on, e.g. put 8 in your head (mime putting a hat on), then count on 3, saying, "8... 9, 10, 11". Keep track of the 3 that your child has counted on, by raising one finger for each number said.

Time

Number these months to show the correct order. One has been done for you.

January = 1	December =	November =
July =	September =	March =
April =	June =	August =
October =	February =	May =

Name a summer month ....

Name a winter month ....

Answers on page 64

Look at these daily events.
Write 'm' below the events that happen in the morning.
Write 'a' below the events that happen in the afternoon.
Write 'n' below the events that happen at night.

PARENT TIP: Refer to o'clock and half-past times and talk about the position of the 'hands' on an analogue clock. Create a visual timetable of things that happen on a school day or weekend and refer to it during the course of the day. Write times alongside events if appropriate.

The zookeeper is looking after the animals. Write down the time in words that he does each job. One has been done for you.

9 o'clock

Answers on page 64

Draw the hands on these clocks to show times of the special events at the zoo.

Seal show
9 o'clock

Bird display
half past 1

Reptile talk
3 o'clock

Ride an elephant
half past 10

Feed a snake
half past 4

Ordinal Numbers

Look at this line of animals waiting to be fed.
The elephant is 1st. Put position stickers next to the animals that are 3rd, 6th, 7th and 9th in the line.

What position are the following animals?

giraffe [ ] zebra [ ] penguin [ ]

Colour the feeding plates in this order:
Red: 1st, 4th
Green: 2nd, 5th
Blue: 3rd, 6th

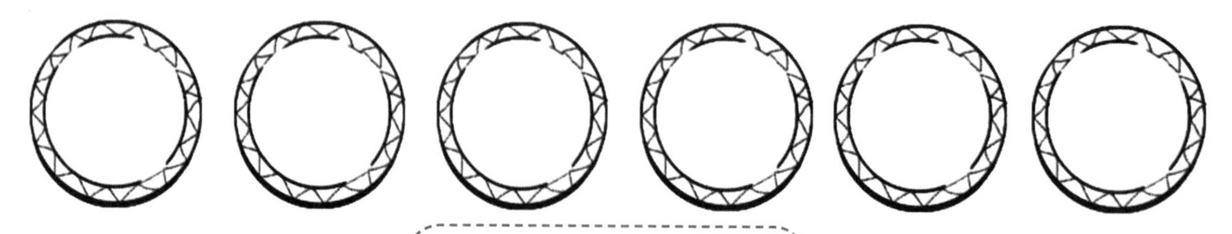

Answers on page 64

PARENT TIP: Use ordinal numbers (1st, 2nd, 3rd, etc.) to describe positions and 'taking turns' at home, e.g. Jamie can get a drink first, then Amanda second. Set up races with friends and award 1st, 2nd and 3rd place medals and certificates.

Odds and Evens

Colour numbers 1, 3 and 5 in red. Carry on colouring every other number in red.

1	2	3	4	5	6	7	8	9	10
11	12	13	14	15	16	17	18	19	20

The red numbers are odd numbers.
The other numbers are even numbers.

Decide if the number of squares in each shape is odd or even by counting how many squares are in each shape. Write 'odd' or 'even' under each one. What do you notice?

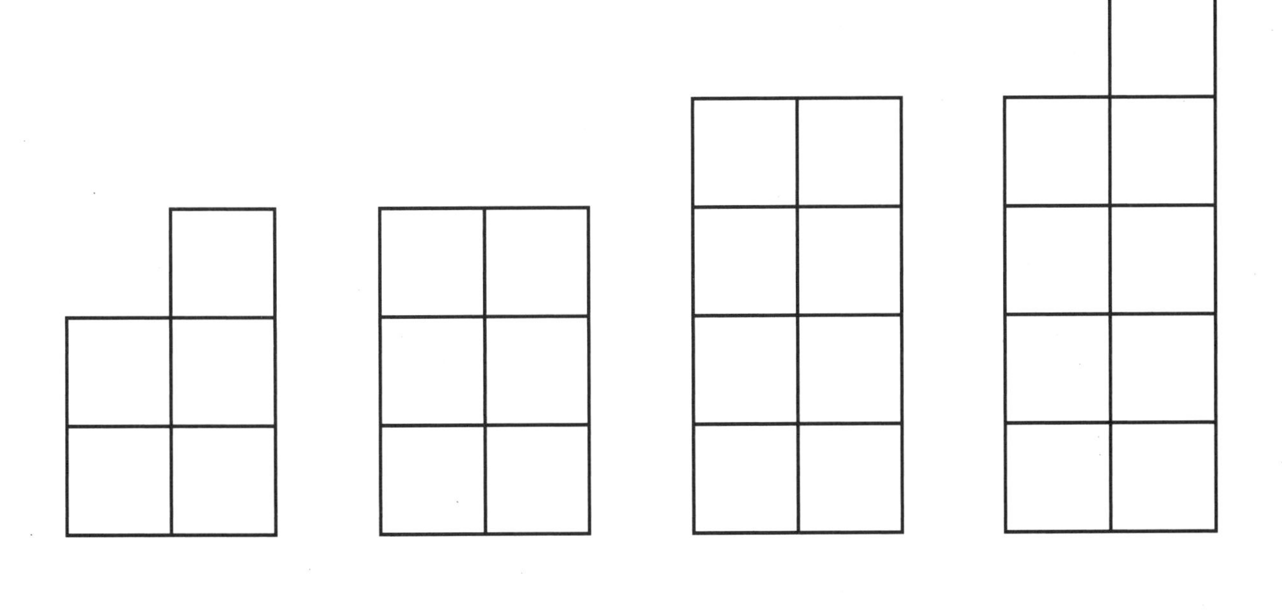

....

Counting Back

This bee flies from flower to flower. Follow the instructions and count back to see where she lands.

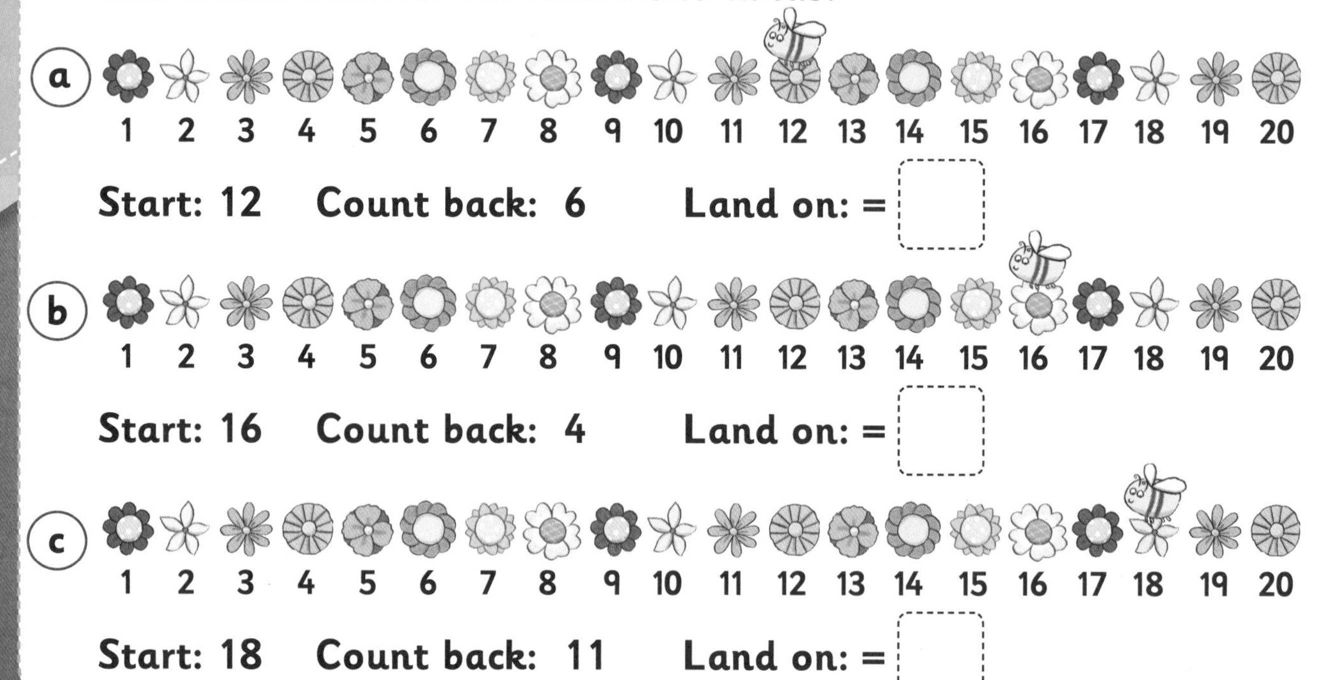

There were 14 bees in this hive. 7 have flown out. How many are left inside?

bees

Answers on page 64

PARENT TIP: Counting back to find answers to subtractions is difficult for children. Use fingers to keep track of the numbers counted back, so they know when to stop. Draw a number track on the garden path with chalk and practise jumping back in 1s from different starting points.

3D Shapes

Here is a set of 3D shapes. Colour the shapes below to match.

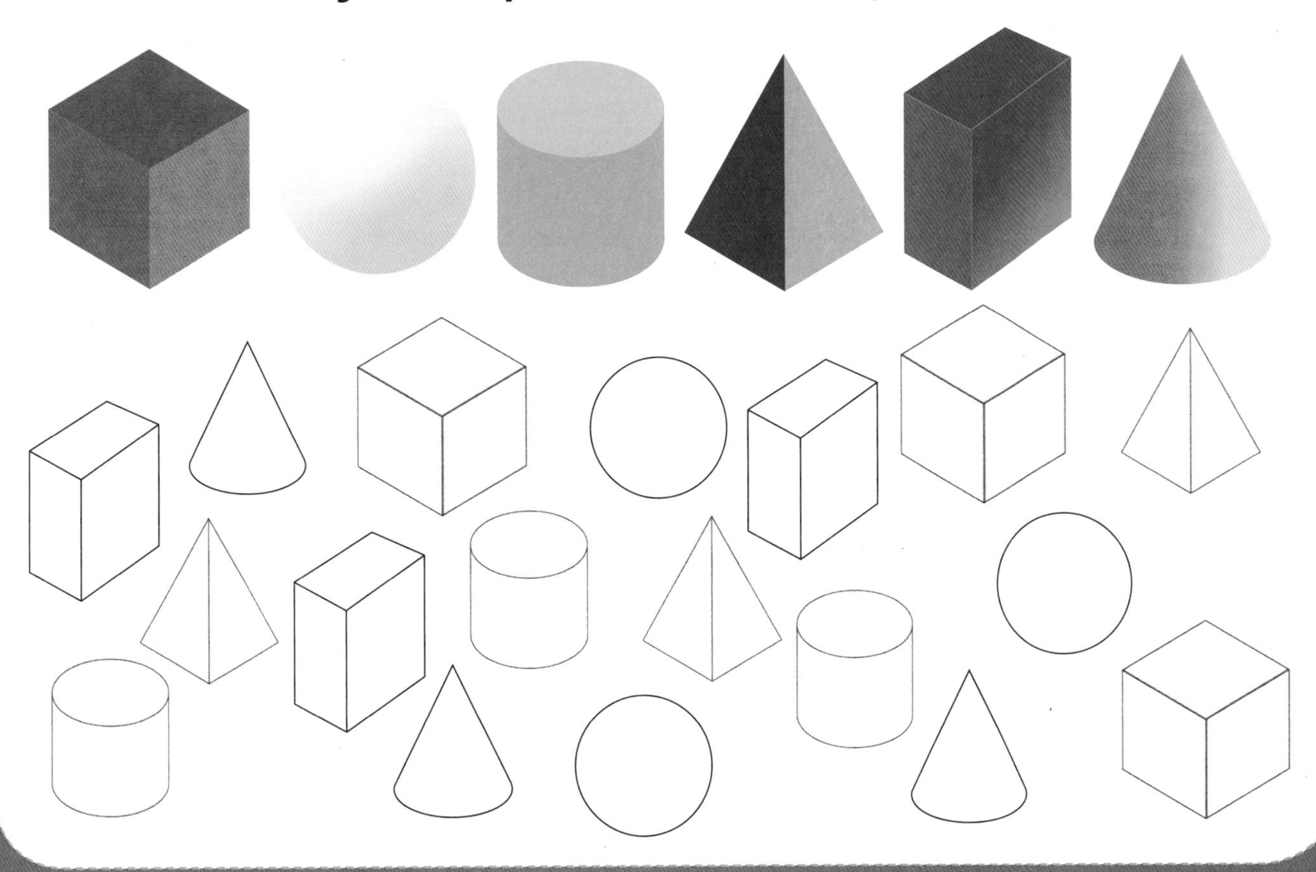

Find the 3D shape stickers and put them in the correct place on this chart.

Shapes that roll	Shapes that do not roll

PARENT TIP: Find some solid 3D shapes, e.g. tissue box for cuboid, baked bean tin for cylinder, dice for cube. Count the faces, edges and vertices. Describe shapes to each other. Can you guess the shape from its description?

Pictograms

Max and Harry went rock-pooling and collected lots of sea creatures. This pictogram shows what they caught.

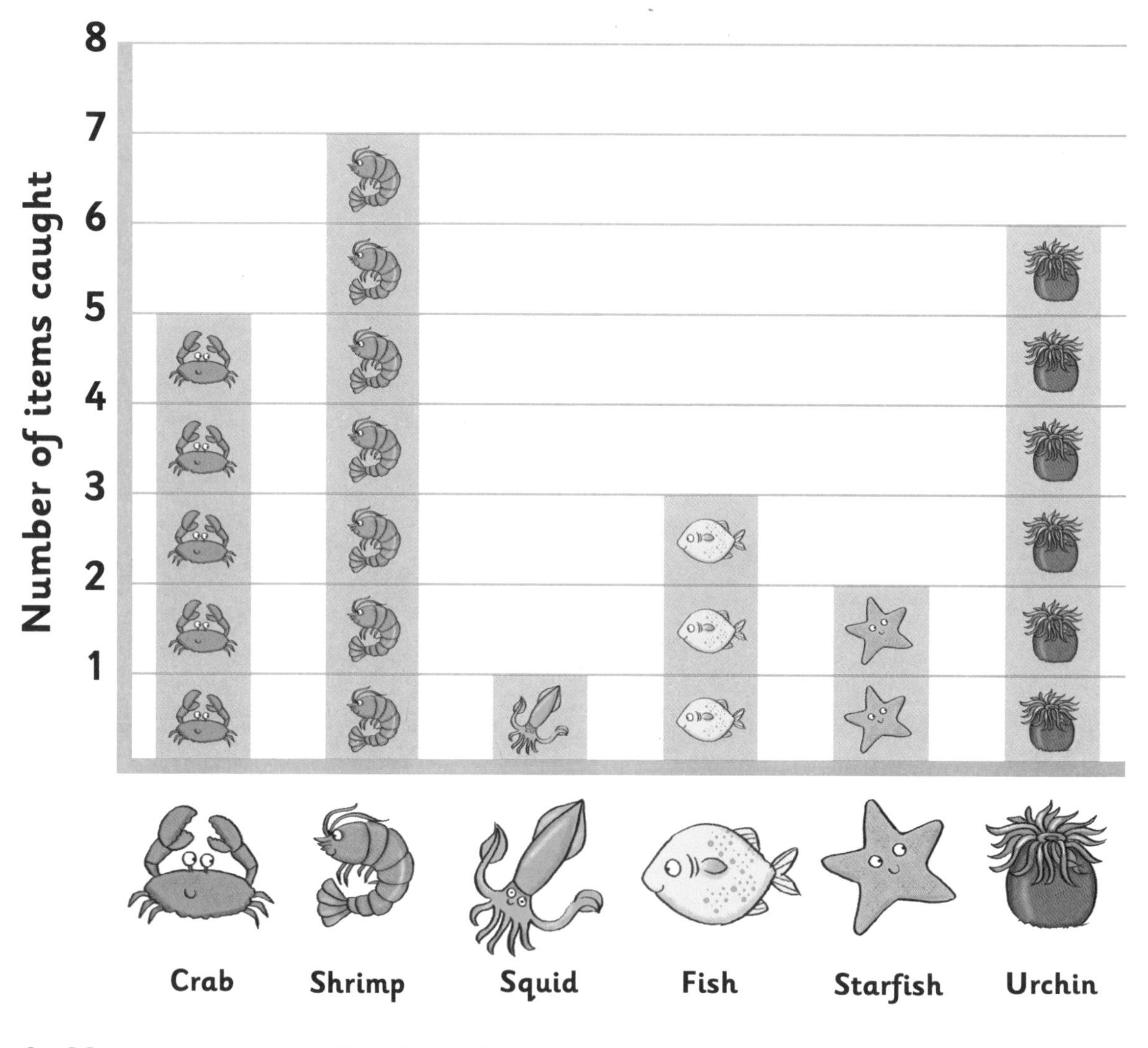

1. How many crabs did they catch? ....

2. Did they catch any fish? How many? ....

3. Which creature did they catch 6 of? ....

4. How many creatures did they catch altogether? ....

Answers on page 64

Amanda asked her friends what pets they owned. She put the information in a chart.

Pet	Number of friends who have one
Fish	3
Dog	2
Cat	5
Lizard	1
Hamster	3

1. Which is the most common pet?

....

2. How many friends own a dog?

....

3. Which pet does only 1 friend own?

....

Answers on page 64

Draw the pets in the pictogram to show Amanda's results.

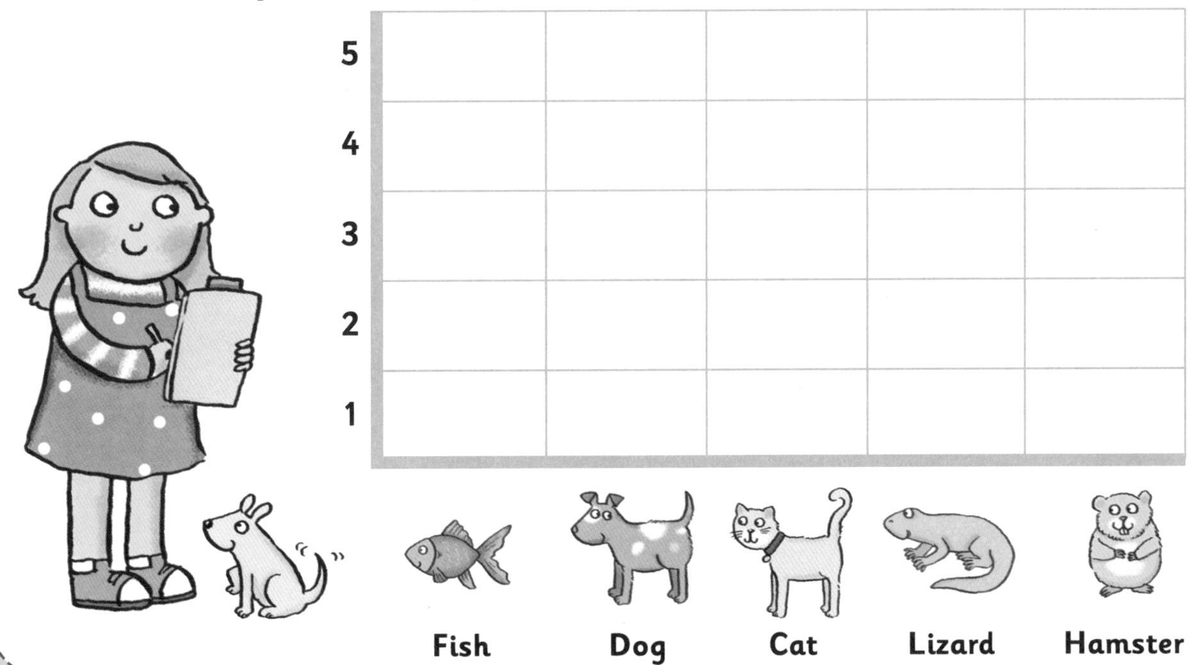

PARENT TIP: Looking at information collected and presented in different ways is very important. Write a list of five colours, then ask family and friends to choose their favourite. Record the information in a chart and then show it as a pictogram.

Numbers to 50

Write the missing numbers on these snakes.

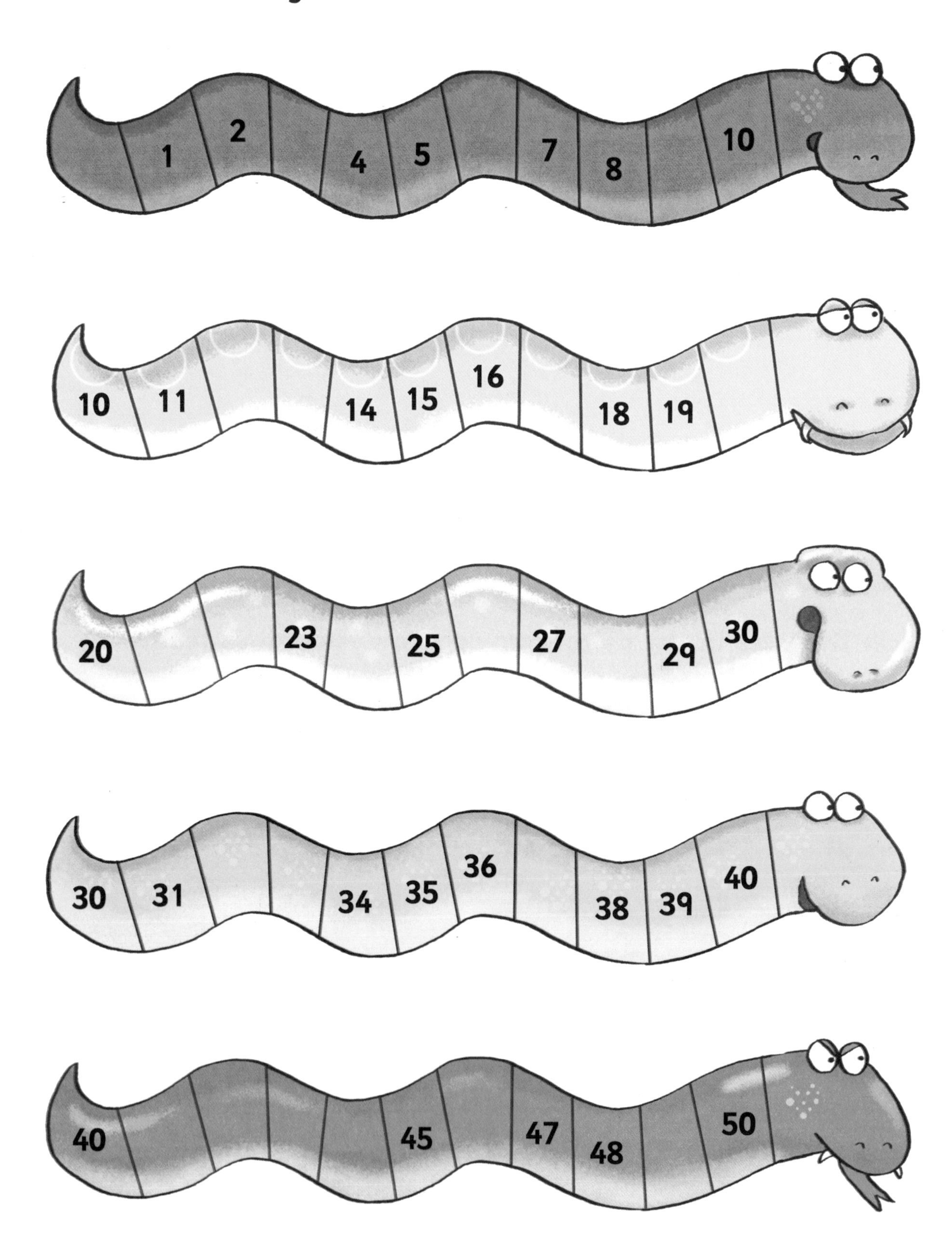

Complete this picture joining the numbers in order.

PARENT TIP: Chanting numbers in order to 50 and beyond is very important. Children need to become familiar with the pattern that repeats each ten. Initially they will need help to 'bridge' to the next ten. Help them over the next ten by chanting together, "30, 31, 32..." and then leave them to continue again by themselves.

Measuring

These divers are learning about sharks. Use a ruler to measure the length of each shark. Write the lengths in the boxes in centimetres, then circle the longest shark.

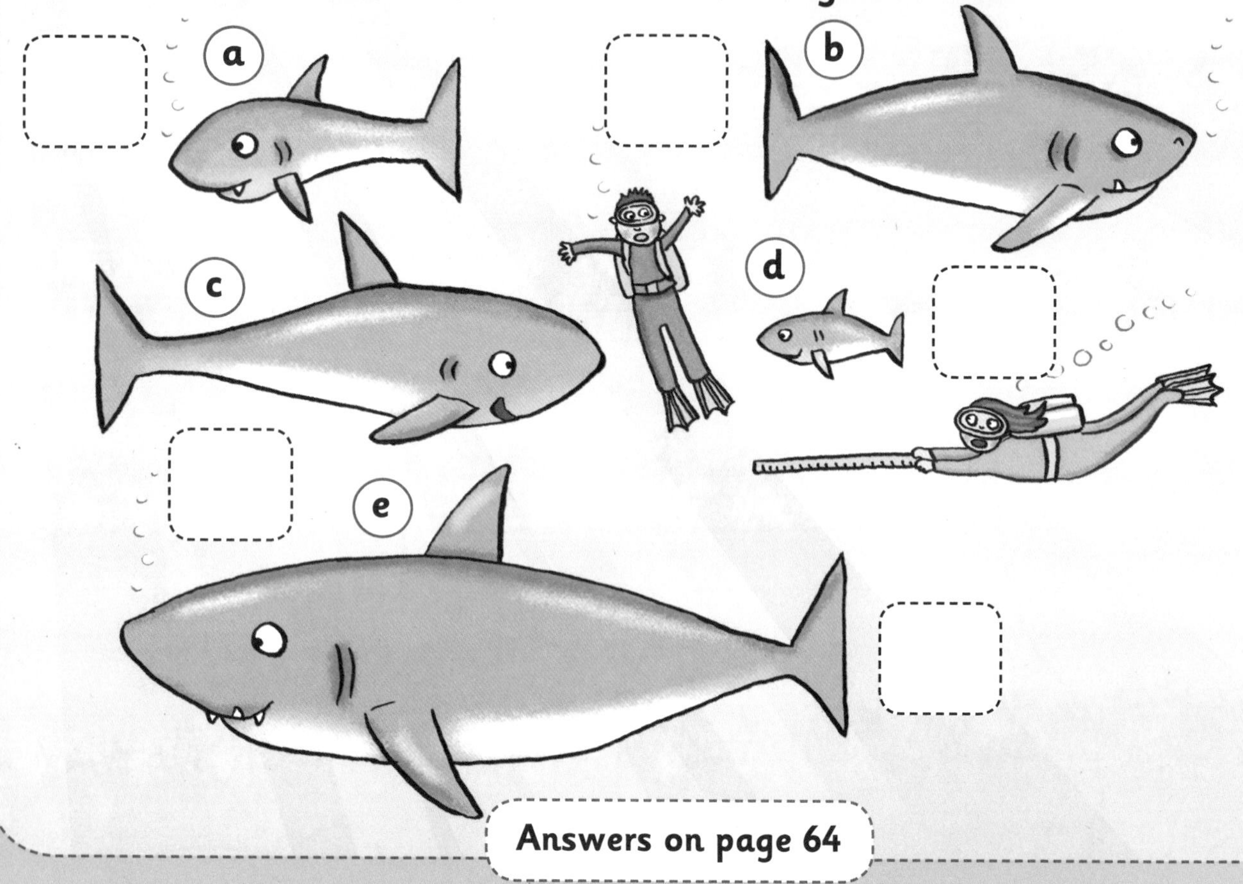

Answers on page 64

Choose the shark stickers that measure 2cm, 4cm and 6cm. Stick them here in order, from shortest to longest.

Now draw your own shark which is 5cm in length.

The divers have weighed the sharks to find the heaviest one. Look at the number that each scale is pointing to and write the weights down as words.

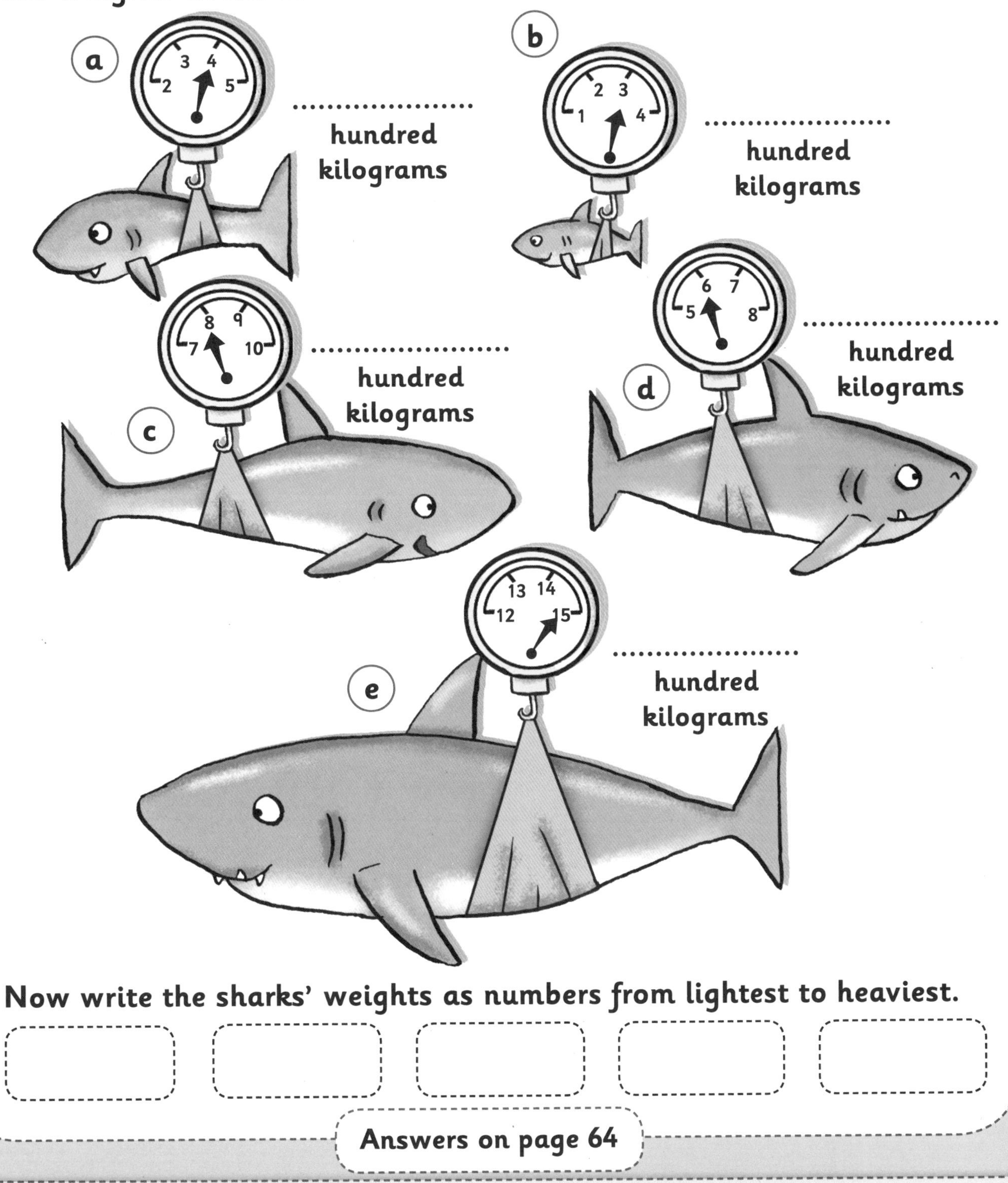

Now write the sharks' weights as numbers from lightest to heaviest.

Answers on page 64

PARENT TIP: Look round the home together to find the shortest, the longest, the tallest, the heaviest and the lightest objects. Hold two items directly against each other to compare their lengths and then hold one in each hand to compare their weights. Begin to use rulers and tape measures to measure objects to the nearest whole centimetre.

Doubling

Read the sentences and then complete the sums below.

Farmer Ted has 2 fields with 3 sheep in each field.

2 x 3 = ☐

Farmer Jack has 2 stables with 4 horses in each stable.

2 x 4 = ☐

Farmer Claire has 2 ponds with 6 ducks on each pond.

2 x 6 = ☐

Join each number to its double.

5 9 7 2

4 14 10 18

Answers on page 64

PARENT TIP: Choose a number to double, e.g. 3. Now slowly turn over cards in a playing card set. The first to spot the double shouts, "Stop!" and wins those cards. Choose a different number and continue the game. Remove cards not in play, e.g. Jack, Queen, King and Aces.

Counting in 2s, 5s and 10s

How many frogs? Count in 2s to find out.

How many fish? Count in 5s to find out.

How many bugs? Count in 10s to find out.

Complete these number sequences.

2	4		8			14
5		15		25		35
10	20		40		60	

Answers on page 64

Counting to 100

Look at the numbers the birds are holding, then find them on the number square on page 59.

Number Order

1	2	3	4	5	6	7	8	9	10
11	12	13	14	15	16	17	18	19	20
21	22	23	24	25	26	27	28	29	30
31	32	33	34	35	36	37	38	39	40
41	42	43	44	45	46	47	48	49	50
51	52	53	54	55	56	57	58	59	60
61	62	63	64	65	66	67	68	69	70
71	72	73	74	75	76	77	78	79	80
81	82	83	84	85	86	87	88	89	90
91	92	93	94	95	96	97	98	99	100

Use the number square to answer these questions.

1. What is 3 more than 40?
2. What is 10 more than 50?
3. What is 5 more than 66?
4. What is 2 less than 80?
5. What is 6 less than 38?
6. What is 4 less than 100?

Answers on page 64

PARENT TIP: Knowing the order of numbers to 100 and finding them on number grids and number lines is a key skill. Practise this by looking for given numbers on tape measures and measuring jugs in the home. Use vocabulary, such as 'before' and 'after', to describe the position of specific numbers in relation to others.

Halves and Quarters

Here are 6 rabbits. Half of the group live in each rabbit hutch. Join the rabbits to their hutches.

Find 8 kitten stickers. Put half of the 8 stickers in each basket.

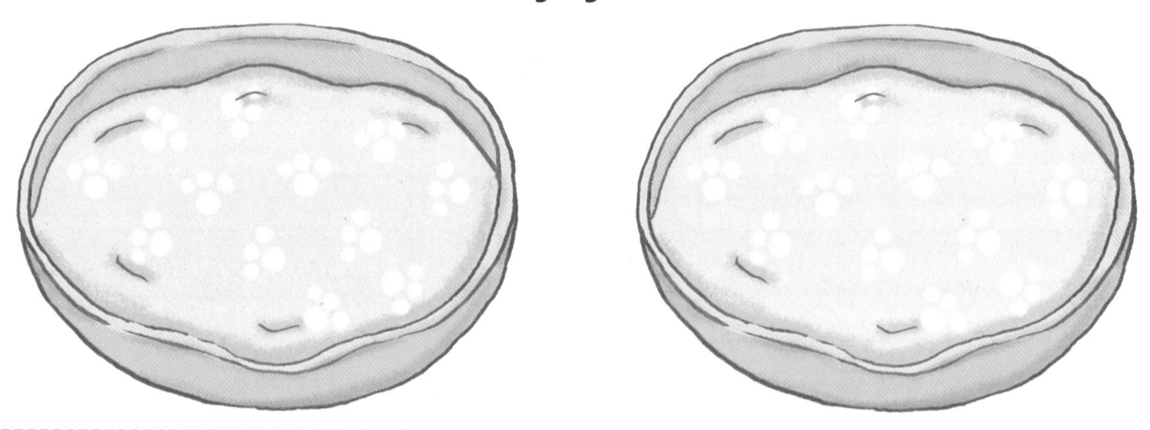

Here is a tank with 10 fish. Colour half of them green and half of them orange. How many are orange?

Answers on page 64

PARENT TIP: Children tend to develop an intuitive understanding of 'half' through sharing. Highlight these 'sharing between two' opportunities and clarify that it needs to be fair and both people need to get the same number. Practise finding half of a number of objects, by sharing them out. Then ask, "how many do we each have?"

Look at the group of bugs below. Circle half of the total number in each set.

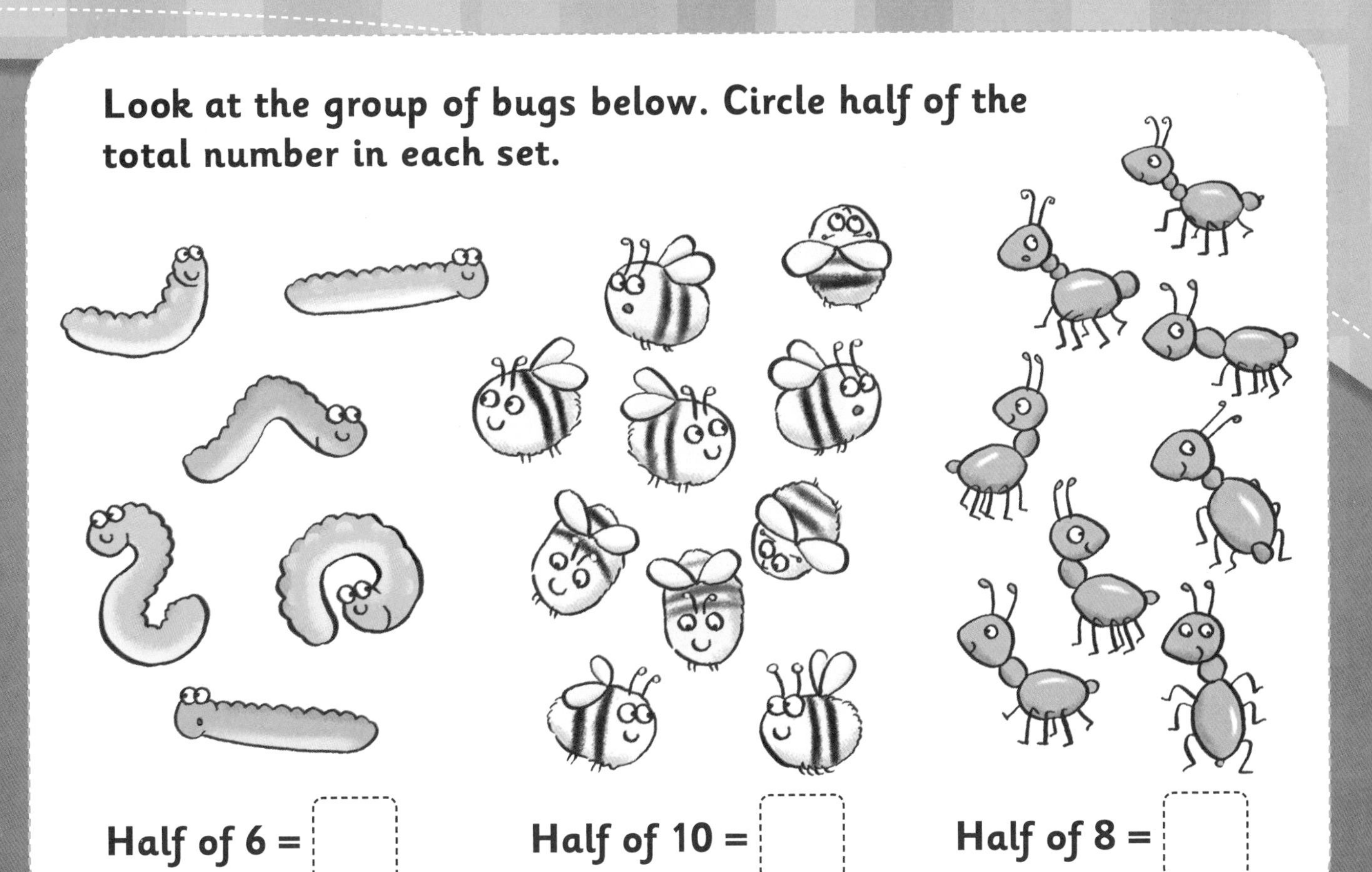

Half of 6 =

Half of 10 =

Half of 8 =

Each child will take home a quarter of these snails. Join the snails to their new owners.

Answers on page 64

Turning

Bill the zookeeper needs to keep watch over all the animals. He stays in the centre and turns clockwise to face each group.

Fill the gaps in the table below.

Start facing	Turn	End facing
giraffes	one quarter turn	
penguins	one half turn	
tigers		giraffes
giraffes	one half turn	
monkeys		tigers
tigers	three quarter turn	
monkeys	one half turn	
giraffes	one whole turn	

Answers on page 64

PARENT TIP: It is very hard for children to visualise turning when it is represented on paper. Place a toy figure in the centre where Bill stands and turn it to face the groups of animals. Play other direction games where you ask your child to make a given turn. Play with a group of children. Those that make a mistake are out. Who is the winner?

Calculation Puzzles

Use the animal code to do these calculations. Write the answers in the boxes.

15 12 10 3 6 8

Answers on page 64

Make up one addition and one subtraction sum yourself using the animal code stickers.

Answers

Page 34: Counting to 20
a – 12, b – 19, c – 15, d – 14, e – 17, f – 13, g – 16, h – 18. There are 18 bugs in the tank.

Page 35: Teen Numbers and Words

Page 36: Make 10

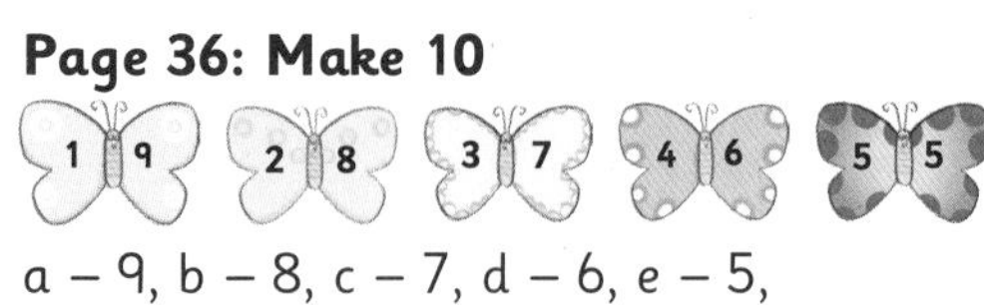

a – 9, b – 8, c – 7, d – 6, e – 5,
f – 1, g – 2, h – 3, i – 4, j – 0

Page 37: Make 20
5 + 15, 6 + 14, 7 + 13, 8 + 12, 9 + 11

Page 38: Money Maths
Purse a = 2p + 2p + 1p + 1p, Purse b = 5p + 1p
Purse c = 2p + 2p + 2p
Piggy bank a = 16p, Piggy bank b = 30p
Piggy bank c = 50p

Page 39: Money Maths (continued)
Basket a – 13p, basket b – 13p, basket c – 18p
Rory gets 8p change, Carly gets 15p change.

Page 40: Missing Number Puzzles
Ant farm a: 14 + 6 = 20 ants
Ant farm b: 4 + 2 = 6 ants
Ant farm c: 8 + 4 = 12 ants
You need to add 16 ant stickers to make 20.

Page 41: Repeating Patterns
Zebra: 1-2-1-2-1-2-1-2
Tiger: 3-6-3-6-3-6-3-6
Monkey: 2-4-6-2-4-6-2-4

Page 42: Counting On to Add
Bridge a: Monkey lands on 9, Bridge b: Monkey lands on 11, Bridge c: Monkey lands on 16, Bridge d: Monkey lands on 16.
There will be 14 monkeys at the party.

Page 43: 2D Shapes
The star has: 5 points and 10 sides

Page 44: Time
January – 1, February – 2, March – 3, April – 4, May – 5, June – 6, July – 7, August – 8, September – 9, October – 10, November – 11, December – 12

Page 45: Time (continued)
Feed the penguins: nine o'clock, Play with the monkeys: ten o'clock, Feed the crocodile: one o'clock Wash the elephant: two o'clock, Feed the tiger: three o'clock, Tidy the penguins: four o'clock

Page 46: Ordinal Numbers
3rd: Tiger, 6th: Monkey, 7th: Rhino, 9th: Lion
Giraffe: 2nd, Zebra: 5th, Penguin: 8th

Page 48: Counting Back
Bee a lands on 6, Bee b lands on 12, Bee c lands on 7.
7 bees are left inside the hive.

Page 50: Pictograms
1. 5 crabs, 2. 3 fish, 3. 6 urchins, 4. 24 creatures

Page 51: Pictograms (continued)
1. Cats are the most common pet, 2. 2 friends own a dog, 3. Only one friend has a lizard.

Page 54: Measuring
Shark a is 4cm, shark b is 6cm, shark c is 7cm, shark d is 2cm, shark e is 10cm

Page 55: Measuring (continued)
a = four hundred kg, b = three hundred kg,
c = eight hundred kg, d = six hundred kg,
e = fifteen hundred kg.
Lightest to heaviest: b – (300 kg), a – (400 kg), d – (600 kg), c – (800 kg), e – (1500 kg)

Page 56: Doubling
2 x 3 = 6, 2 x 4 = 8, 2 x 6 = 12
5 – 10, 9 – 18, 7 – 14, 2 – 4

Page 57: Counting in 2s, 5s and 10s
8 frogs, 15 fish, 40 bugs
2 4 6 8 10 12 14, 5 10 15 20 25 30 35,
10 20 30 40 50 60 70

Page 59: Number Order
1. 43, 2. 60, 3. 71, 4. 78, 5. 32, 6. 96

Page 60: Halves and Quarters
5 fish are orange

Page 61: Halves and Quarters (continued)
Half of 6 = 3, half of 10 = 5, half of 8 = 4
Each child takes home 3 snails.

Page 62: Turning

Start facing	Turn	End facing
giraffes	one quarter turn	penguins
penguins	one half turn	tigers
tigers	one quarter turn	giraffes
giraffes	one half turn	monkeys
monkeys	one quarter turn	tigers
tigers	three quarter turn	monkeys
monkeys	one half turn	giraffes
giraffes	one whole turn	giraffes

Page 63: Calculation Puzzles
a = 2, b = 9, c = 25, d = 23

6-7 years

Leap Ahead

BUMPER Workbook

Key Stage 1

ENGLISH

Home learning made FUN!

Where Do You Live?

Write about the place that you live using the adjectives (describing words) below to help you.

big, small, warm, cosy, friendly, old, new, busy, modern, colourful, tidy

Describe your home and draw a picture:

....

....

....

....

....

....

....

Describe a room in your home and draw a picture:

....

....

....

....

....

....

....

What's the Order?

Tom's books have fallen on the floor. Put them back in alphabetical order by numbering them from 1–7. The first one has been done for you.

Put these party invitations in alphabetical order by numbering them from 1–6. The first one has been done for you.

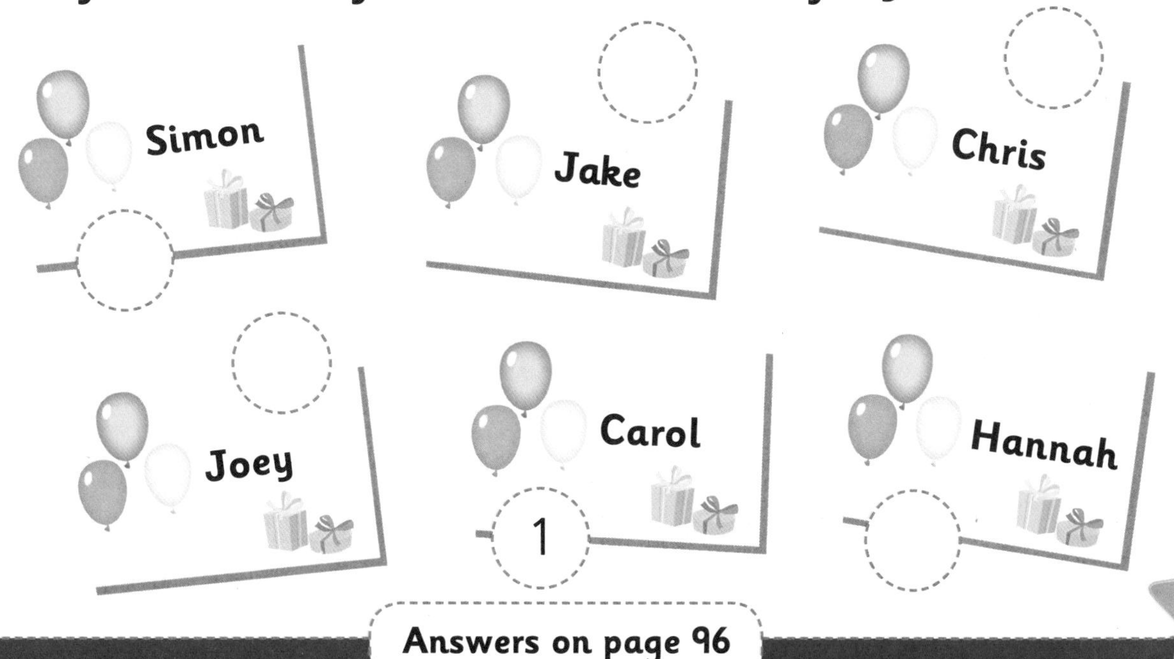

Answers on page 96

Super Spellings

Choose the correct letters from the box below to complete each of these sentences. Each letter combination is used more than once. The first one is done for you.

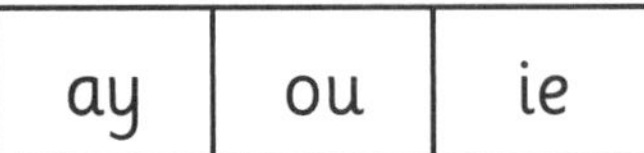

ay	ou	ie

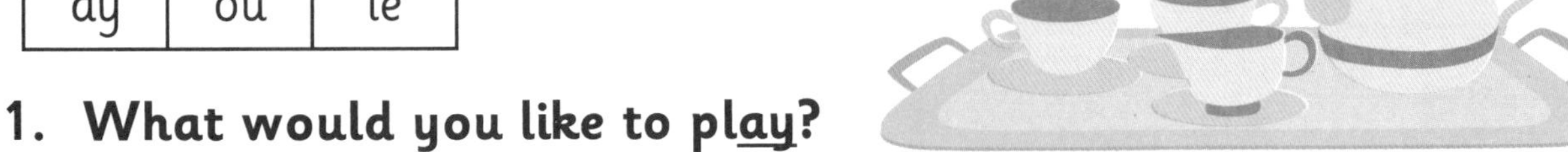

1. **What would you like to play?**
2. **My h........ se is the one on the corner.**
3. **I need to t........ a knot in the wool.**

4. **The tr........ was heavy with cups and mugs on it.**
5. **Do you know anything ab........ t bees?**
6. **That chicken p........ was delicious.**

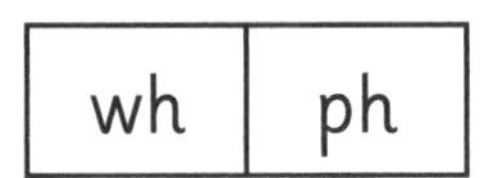

wh	ph

1. **Last night we saw a dolphin swimming in the bay.**
2. **It was late ....en I got back and Mum asked ....ere I had been.**
3. **He grabbed the ....eel of the car.**
4. **An ele........ant never forgets ....ich way to go.**
5. **The little girl was an or........ an who lived with her uncle and aunt.**
6. **I don't know ....ich hat to wear, the red one or the ....ite one.**

Answers on page 96

Pancake Perfection

Look at the pictures showing how to make pancakes. Write an instruction to go with each picture. Can you write a list of ingredients on the shopping list at the bottom?

1 Weigh the flour.
Put it into a mixing bowl.

4oz

2 ....
....
....

3 ....
....
....

4 ....
....
....

Ingredients

1. ....

2. ....

3. ....

4. ....

PARENT TIP: When we write instructions, we often start each sentence with a verb or doing word, such as 'weigh' or 'put'. This is called the 'imperative' or 'command' form.

Fact or Fiction?

Fiction books are stories or make-believe. Non-fiction means facts or information. Draw a line to match up each book with the correct label. One has been done for you.

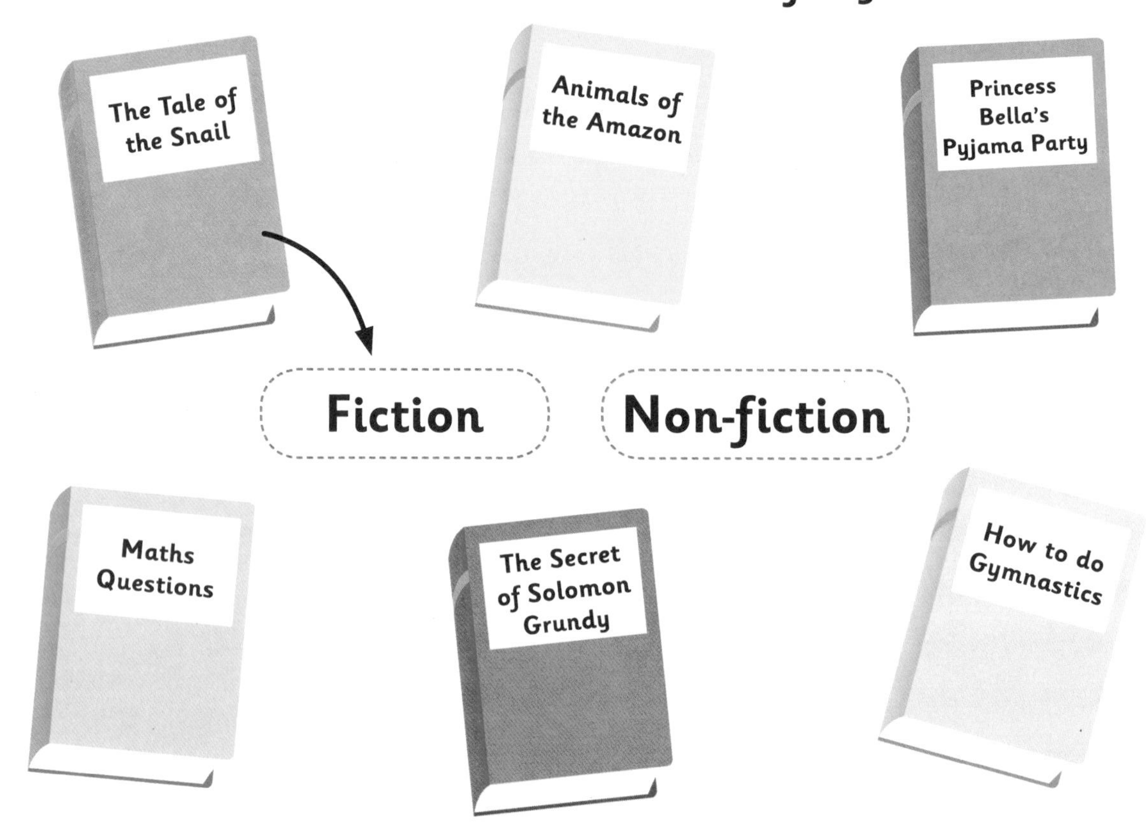

Read these sentences. Write F in the box if the sentence comes from a fiction book. Write N if it comes from a non-fiction book.

1. Coal, oil and gas are all found under the ground. N
2. When George and his pet dragon woke up, they found the whole kingdom of Merridale had turned pink.
3. Then the magic began. The three girls were taken up into the air in a big swirl of golden dust.
4. The Amazon is home to many kinds of mammals, as well as fish and birds.
5. Sunil opened the door. Outside was a smiling man in a battered old hat.
6. Some houses are built from bricks and stone, others from wood.

Answers on page 96

Rhymes and Tongue-twisters

A tongue-twister is a type of rhyme or poem where lots of the words start with the same sound or letter. Try saying this well known tongue-twister as fast as you can!

Peter Piper picked a peck of pickled pepper.
A peck of pickled pepper Peter Piper picked.
If Peter Piper picked a peck of pickled pepper,
Where's the pickled pepper Peter Piper picked?

Use these boxes of words that start with the same letter to write your own tongue-twister on a separate piece of paper.

'p' words:
pink, pat, pig, play, pin, point, pass, past, pong, paint, pet, peas, penny

'g' words:
goat, gate, get, game, great, garden, gang, give, goose

Silly rhymes use a lot of rhyming words together. Say this rhyme and then try to write your own silly rhyme on a separate piece of paper, using the words in the boxes.

A noisy noise
annoys an oyster most.

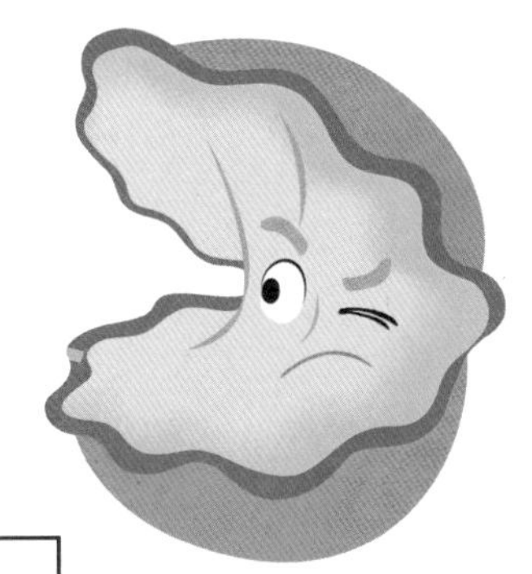

play, say, day, tray, way, hooray, stray, sway

pong, song, long, wrong, ding-dong

Colour the Sounds

Colour the words in the grid below using this colour key:

'oh' sound	'or' sound	'oo' sound
e.g. 'window', 'toe'	e.g. 'floor', 'claw'	e.g. 'chew', 'glue'

true	boat	window	hollow	throw	ball
clue	row	arrow	mow	show	claw
two	tissue	toe	hoe	snore	caught
chew	threw	no	snow	four	law
crew	glue	slow	echo	your	sore
too	flew	coat	goes	floor	raw
who	sue	low	float	saw	roar
blue	brew	so	know	taught	short
drew	knew	solo	hello	daughter	talk
shoe	stew	goat	bow	pour	hall

How many words have you coloured...

... blue?

... yellow?

... purple?

What letter shape can you see in the yellow words?

....

Answers on page 96

PARENT TIP: At this stage in their phonics, children are learning that one sound can be spelt in different ways. The three vowel sounds above can be represented by several different letter combinations, or graphemes.

A Correct Ending

Choose the correct ending from the boxes below to complete each word. Find matching stickers for the last four words and place them in the correct boxes.

al	el	il	le

penc il.......... met.......... padd..........

lev.......... pan.......... trav..........

anim.......... foss.......... bott..........

litt.......... hot.......... nostr..........

smi.......... sca..........

parc.......... app..........

Answers on page 96

PARENT TIP: Children find it difficult to remember which ending is which on words like this. Encourage them to notice word endings when they are reading, so that they can apply this to spelling.

Compound Nouns

Choose the correct word to complete each compound noun jigsaw. The first one has been done for you.

place	ground	stand	~~yard~~

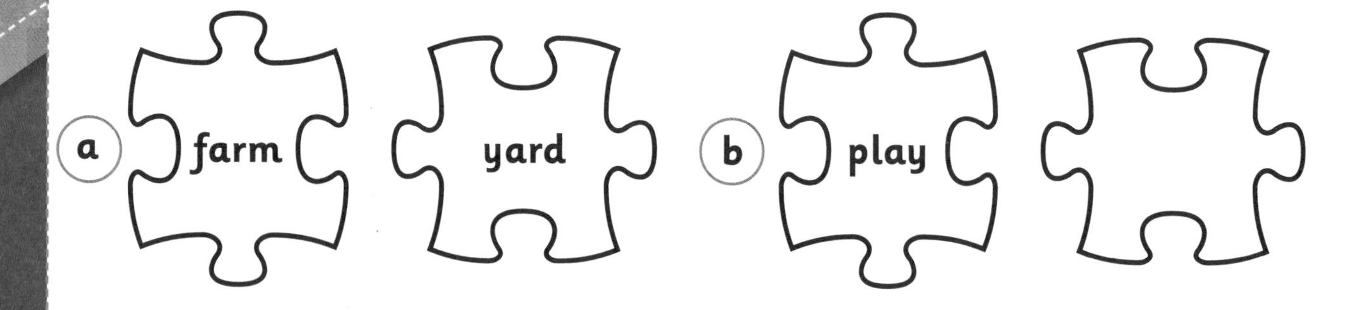

farmyard ....

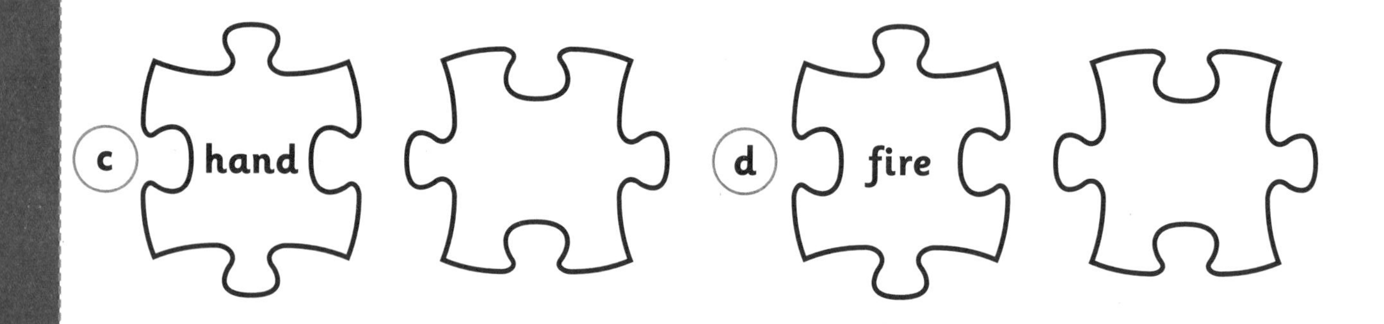

....

Guess these compound nouns from the picture jigsaws.

.... dresser

wind ....

Answers on page 96

Circus Spellings

Read these high-frequency words. Cover each word after you read it, then write it on a separate piece of paper. Check to see if you spelt it right. Finally, add some circus stickers.

our
little
once
who
called
Friday
people
over
eleven
some
down
twenty
because
twice
Sunday
sixteen
brother
yellow
where
twelve
Saturday
Tuesday
school
white
Monday
door
black
sister
would
your

Which Way to the Cinema?

Write directions from home to the cinema using the words in the box to help you. The first one has been done for you.

past, left, right, straight on, turn, go, around, over, cross, walk, along, corner, road

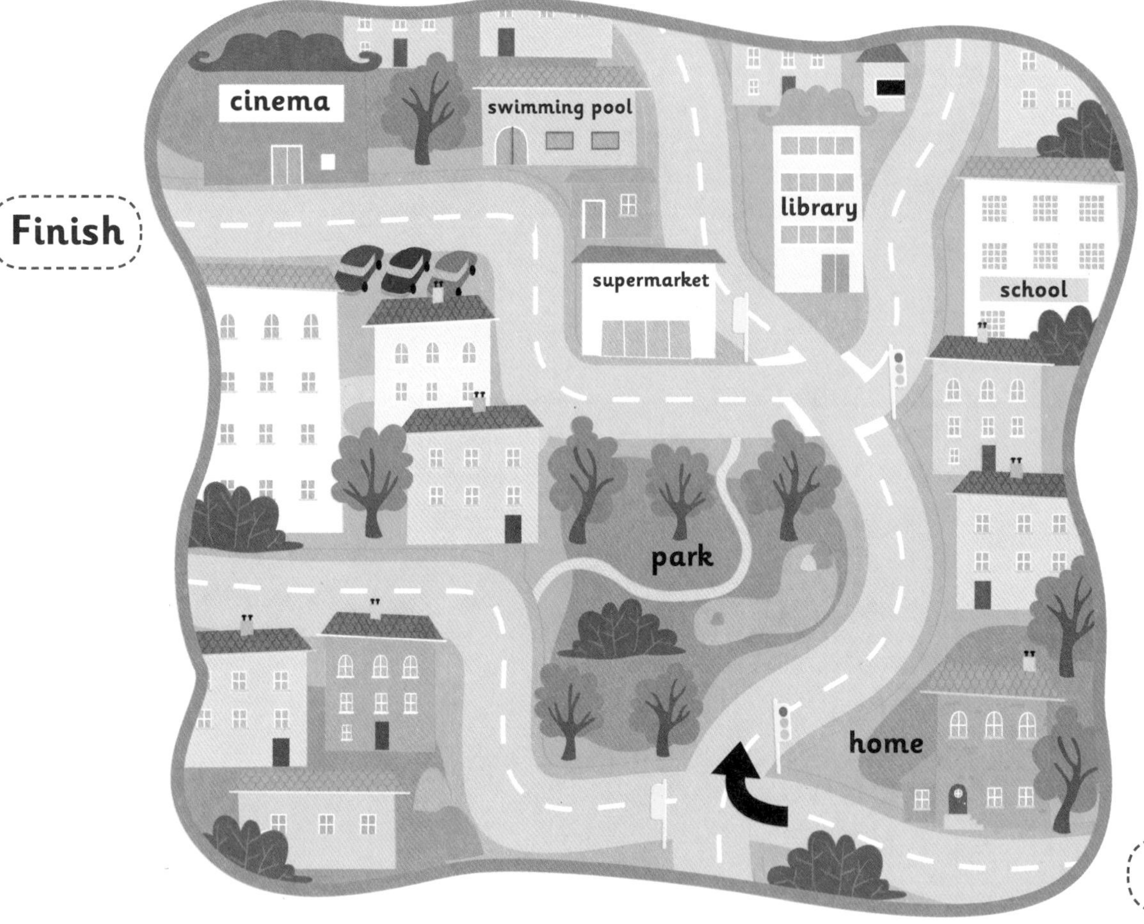

Finish

Start

Directions:

After leaving the house, turn right. Walk along the street to the corner.

....

....

....

....

....

....

Fudge Mix

Find the words ending with 'ge' or 'dge' in the wordsearch. Write each word you find in the correct list underneath.

~~judge~~, huge, nudge, fudge, large, surge, cage, badge, merge, sledge, ~~wage~~

j	u	d	g	e	n	j	h
f	m	d	i	v	u	w	u
u	b	l	t	q	d	a	g
d	c	a	c	m	g	g	e
g	h	r	h	i	e	e	h
e	j	g	a	r	c	h	c
s	l	e	d	g	e	d	a
s	u	r	g	e	h	h	g
b	f	k	b	a	d	g	e
o	l	m	e	r	g	e	h

'ge' words

wage

....

....

....

....

....

'dge' words

judge

....

....

....

....

....

Answers on page 96

PARENT TIP: The 'dge' spelling comes after a short vowel, whereas 'ge' comes after a long vowel sound.

I Spy Spellings

Sophie is having a wonderful dream. Look at all the things she is dreaming about and write them under the correct phonemes below. Some have been done for you.

donkey, game, thief, ~~tray~~, sky, monkey, crayons, slide, field, tie, snake, ~~sea~~, prize, pie, ~~rice~~

'ay' (as in same)	'ee' (as in funny)	'igh' (as in reply)
tray	sea	rice

Answers on page 96

PARENT TIP: Remember that two words can contain the same phoneme (sound) without having the same letters, e.g. 'dry'/'cried'. The phonemes in this activity can be spelt in several different ways.

What Happened Next?

Number the boxes to put the story in the correct order.

a So the little sparrow went to see Robin. "I'd like a nice, red chest like yours," the sparrow said. "Well," said Robin, "to get a nice red chest like mine you must find and eat the reddest berries."

b Once upon a time, there was a little sparrow who was very unhappy. "I'm bored with being a small, brown bird," he told the other sparrows in the old barn. "I want to be a beautiful bird with colourful feathers." 1

c The other birds clustered around him as he told his sad tale. "You may not be beautiful like a robin, or a flamingo," said his mum, "but you will always be beautiful to us, just because we love you." The little sparrow smiled. At last, he really did feel beautiful.

d Sparrow wasn't keen on berries, so he went away to ask the flamingos in the zoo. They were huge and pink with long, graceful necks. Sparrow went to the most beautiful of the birds. "I want to be beautiful, like you," he said.

e "That's easy," said the flamingo. "You must eat little pink shrimps all day." That didn't sound easy to Sparrow. He didn't like shrimps at all! Sparrow began to feel sad. "I will never be beautiful like the robin, or the flamingo," he thought. He flew back to the old barn, where his friends and family were perched.

Answers on page 96

Silent Letters

Write the correct silent letter (k, g or w) at the beginning of each word. Then draw a line to join each word to the sweet treat with the same letter. One has been done for you.

Answers on page 96

Who Said That?

Add speech marks in the correct places below to show the direct speech in each example. Join each word box to the correct person. The first one has been done for you.

a

b

1 "I started work early today as I want to finish Mr Jenkins' new shed," says Mr Trowell the builder. "Then I am off to do a job at the railway station."

2 Today I am going to make some beautiful sponge cakes for my restaurant, says head chef Mr Baker. I hope the customers like them.

3 I am very busy today. I have to look at George's sore throat, and then check Mrs Hagan's bad knee, said Dr Smith. Then I might have a break and a cup of tea.

c

d

4 I take Mr Tickles for a walk in the park every day, said Mrs Pinkson. When we get home I give him a biscuit.

Answers on page 96

Shorten It

Look at the words in the bubbles. Each one can be shortened with an apostrophe. Write the short version at the side with the apostrophe in the correct place.

~~is not~~

should not

did not

had not

do not

cannot

would not

will not

Short version

isn't

....

....

....

....

....

....

....

Now add apostrophes to the names below to show that the objects belong to them.

Mias book

Georges pen

Hannahs desk

Answers on page 96

PARENT TIP: Encourage your child to think about the times that they use these forms in speech. For example, what does 'don't' mean? Are there any times when it's wrong to shorten words like this?

What a Question!

Decide whether each of these sentences needs a full stop or a question mark at the end. The first one has been done for you.

1. Do you know which road I should take to get to the college?
2. I need to know the answer to this question immediately_
3. This is the best time of year to plant tomatoes_

4. How do you know that this is the best time_ Is it because it is sunny_
5. What do you know about cooking_ This cake has come out all wrong_
6. When the long hand reaches twelve, I will start the clock_

Choose a question word from the box to start each sentence. The first one has been done for you.

When	What	How	Where	Which	~~Do~~

1. Do you know the way to the hospital?
2. .... is the cheese that I was saving for my sandwich?
3. .... do I put this tent up? It has no pegs.
4. .... is your dog called? Mine is called Fido.
5. .... is it time to open the presents?
6. .... is the right hat?

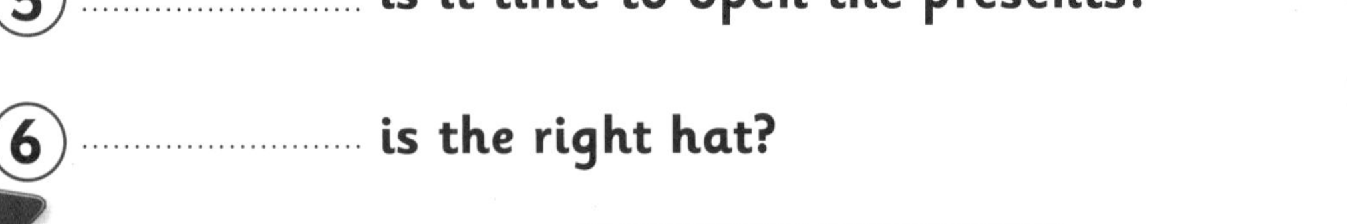

Answers on page 96

A Sound Landing

Look at the phonemes in the box and read the words in the grid. Decide which phoneme can be found in each word and colour the words to match the phonemes. Which phoneme pathway leads to Earth?

'ur' sound as in girl	'eer' sound as in spear

Start

curtain	girl	gear	steer	first	ear
hear	worse	earth	worth	hurl	fur
sheer	deer	whirl	curl	spear	tear
career	cheer	leer	her	certain	shirt
beer	fear	near	here	hurt	burst
skirt	dear	bird	worm	birth	insert
year	third	herb	perky	pearl	person

Finish

This kangaroo can only land on words that have the phoneme 'air', as in 'bear'. Draw a circle around each word with an 'air' sound.

Start

wear	wing	nowhere	about
bear	air	where	hare
face	know	twig	care
rare	whale	please	stare

Finish

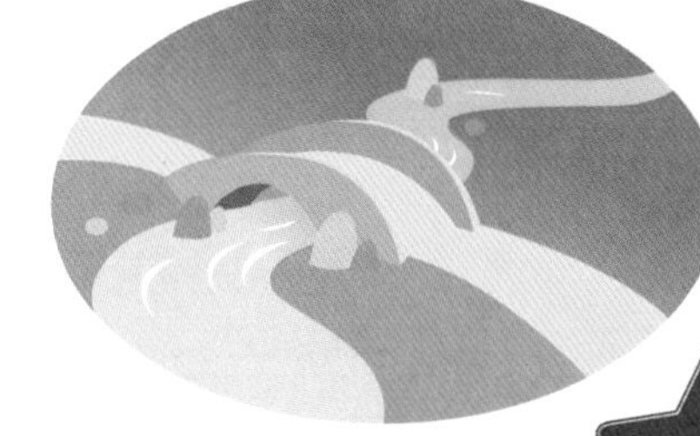

Can the kangaroo jump across the grid to reach the stream? ☐

Answers on page 96

Then There Were More

When we want to say that there is more than one of something, we use the 'plural'. For example, the plural of sweet is 'sweets'. Read these sentences and decide which words need to be made plural by adding 's' or 'es'.

1. When I woke up the room was filled with presents and cards sending me best wishes.
2. I love riding horse..... and this one is my favourite. I visit him in the stable..... with some oat..... every day.
3. Tom was bragging that he had two watch..... . One watch had hand..... on it and the other was digital.
4. I tried to put the light on but there were so many switch..... that I couldn't find the right one. It was so dark I couldn't see my own finger.....!
5. There are probably many planet..... , moon..... , star..... and other thing..... in space that we have not yet seen.

When a word ends in 'y', we don't add just 's' or 'es'. Cross out the 'y' and replace it with 'ies' to make the words in these sentences plural. One has been done for you.

1. I love babies, but their crying hurts my ears.
2. Please don't drop the jelly..... . They have only just set.
3. I thought I could hear some cry..... for help, but it was only a seagull.
4. Those lady..... over there have the nicest cakes.

Answers on page 96

Suffix Detective

Finish the words with the correct spelling by adding the suffix 'ing' or 'ed'. Add a detective's magnifying glass sticker above each suffix once you have written it correctly.

I was walk........ down the street. I had a few moments to wait,

so I push........ my way into the café.

I bought my coffee and turn........ to sit down. I spott........ a man

who was sitt........ with a blue book. He was read........ quietly,

but something about him made me keep watch.........

Then he look........ at me. He star.........

He stood up suddenly, spill........ his coffee. Why did he get up

so quickly? Where was he go.........?

I stirr......... my coffee and took a last sip.

Then I got up and follow......... him.

Answers on page 96

Find the Hidden Treasure

Read the clues and follow the directions to find the hidden treasure. Check your answer at the back of the book and put a treasure chest sticker in the right place on the grid.

1. **Steer your ship to the beach at E10.**
2. **Walk up four spaces.**
3. **Oh, no! Crocodile! Go three spaces to the left.**
4. **Try to cross the volcano by going down one space and three spaces to the left.**
5. **Go down two spaces to avoid the lava.**
6. **Oh, no! Quicksand! Go down two spaces and go two spaces to the left, then rest for a few seconds in the cave.**
7. **It's a dragon's cave! Run out of the cave and go up two spaces to find the treasure.**

....

....

	1	2
A		
B		
C		
D		
E		
F		
G		

Can you think of a name for this island? Write it in the box below the directions, then add some more trees, plants, rocks and flamingos to the scene using the stickers on the sticker sheet.

4	5	6	7	8	9	10	11	12

Answer on page 96

Hide Your Own Treasure

Decide where to hide your own treasure on this grid and draw a map. Write your own instructions to someone else to help them find it. Use imperatives, e.g. 'Walk three spaces to the left'.

	1	2	3	4	5	6	7
A							
B							
C							
D							
E							
F							
G							

To find the treasure...

....

....

....

....

....

....

....

....

Haunted House

Read this spooky poem out loud:

Haunted house on the hill,
Windows dark and curtains still,
Rooms asleep in quiet chill.

Through the doorway, in you sneak,
Down the hall, the floorboards creak.

Up the stairs, the portraits shift,
An old clock chimes, the curtains drift.

Look around, what's hiding here?
Is it just the dark you fear?

Listen hard, a step behind...
Some things are best not to find.

Haunted house on the hill,
All awake and waiting, still.

Can you write a short poem about a creepy house like this one? Use the picture and the rhyming words in the box to help you.

creak	sneak	chill	shrill	old	cold
gloom	room	stairs	hairs	dark	spark

....

....

....

....

....

....

....

....

....

Monster Crossword

Complete the crossword all about this monster.

Across

1. This monster scratches his head with his <u>claws</u>.
5. The monster's eyes are .... shaped.
6. The monster has .... arms, like a spider.
7. He has a long nose, or ....
9. This monster's ears are round, or ....

Down

2. This monster's head is <u>lumpy</u>.
3. The monster has long .... on his chin.
4. His fur is the colour ....
8. The monster is the opposite of beautiful!

1 c	2 l	a	3 w	s				4 g
	u							
	m							
	p		5 s			a		
	y							n
			6	i			t	
			7 s			8 u		
		9 c					e	
						y		

Answers on page 96

Alien Anagrams

Unscramble these alien names to make everyday words. Draw lines to join each anagram to the correct words and find the missing stickers.

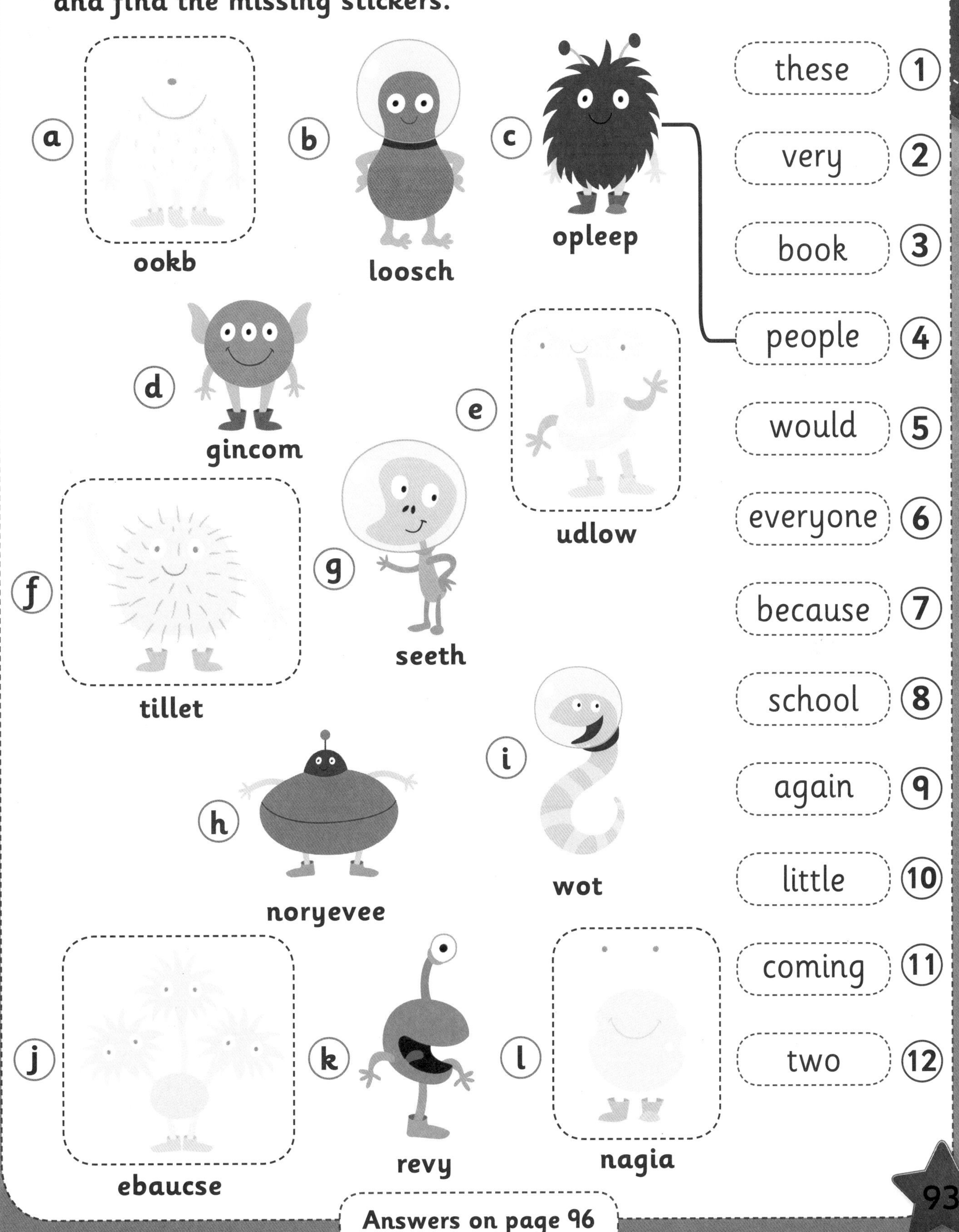

Answers on page 96

My Diary

Write a short diary of your typical week.

Think about the weekdays,
the weekends and the things
you get up to at particular times.

Place a star sticker by your favourite days
of the week.

Monday ....

....

....

....

....

Tuesday ....

....

....

....

....

Wednesday ....

....

....

....

....

Thursday

Friday

Saturday

Sunday

Answers

Page 67: What's the Order?
1 - Dinosaurs, 2 - Dogs, 3 - Lizards and Reptiles, 4 - Moths and Butterflies, 5 - Sea Creatures, 6 - Space Travel, 7 - Stick Insects
1 - Carol, 2 - Chris, 3 - Hannah, 4 - Jake, 5 - Joey, 6 - Simon

Page 68: Super Spellings
1 - play, 2 - house, 3 - tie, 4 - tray, 5 - about, 6 - pie. 1 - dolphin, 2 - when/where, 3 - wheel 4 - elephant/which, 5 - orphan, 6 - which/white

Page 70: Fact or Fiction?
The Tale of the Snail: fiction, Animals of the Amazon: non-fiction, Princess Bella's Pyjama Party: fiction, Maths Questions: non-fiction, The Secret of Solomon Grundy: fiction, How to do Gymnastics: non-fiction
1 - N, 2 - F, 3 - F, 4 - N, 5 - F, 6 - N

Page 72: Colour the Sounds
18 blue words. 24 yellow words. 18 purple words. The yellow words make the letter shape 'T'.

Page 73: A Correct Ending
pencil/metal/paddle/level/panel/travel/animal/fossil/bottle/little/hotel/nostril/smile/scale/parcel/apple

Page 74: Compound Nouns
a: farmyard, b: playground, c: handstand, d: fireplace, e: hairdresser, f: windscreen

Page 77: Fudge Mix

j	u	d	g	e	n	j	h
f	m	d	i	v	u	w	u
u	b	l	t	q	d	a	g
d	c	a	c	m	g	g	e
g	h	r	h	i	e	e	h
e	j	g	a	r	c	h	c
s	l	e	d	g	e	d	a
s	u	r	g	e	h	h	g
b	f	k	b	a	d	g	e
o	l	m	e	r	g	e	h

'ge' words: wage, huge, large, surge, cage, merge

'dge' words: judge, nudge, fudge, badge, sledge

Pages 78–79: I Spy Spellings
'ay' words – tray, crayons, game, snake.
'ee' words – sea, field, thief, monkey, donkey
'igh' words – rice, pie, tie, slide, prize, sky

Page 80: What Happened Next?
a – 2, b – 1, c – 5, d – 3, e – 4

Page 81: Silent Letters
gnome/gnat/knight/knot/knife/wrap/write/wrong/written/writer/wrote/wrist/knees/gnash/knock/whole

Page 82: Who Said That?
a - 3, b - 4, c - 1, d - 2

Page 83: Shorten It
is not - isn't / did not - didn't / should not - shouldn't / had not - hadn't / do not - don't / cannot - can't / would not - wouldn't / will not - won't
Mia's book / George's pen / Hannah's desk

Page 84: What a Question!
1 ? 2 . 3 . 4 ? ? 5 ? . 6 .
1 - Do 2 - Where 3 - How 4 - What
5 - When 6 - Which

Page 85: A Sound Landing
The 'ur' (yellow) pathway leads to Earth.
Yes, the kangaroo can reach the stream.

Page 86: Then There Were More
1 - presents/cards/wishes 2 - horses/stables/oats 3 - watches/hands 4 - switches/fingers 5 - planets/moons/stars/things

1 - babies 2 - jellies 3 - cries 4 - ladies

Page 87: Suffix Detective
I was walking down the street. I had a few moments to wait, so I pushed my way into the café. I bought my coffee and turned to sit down. I spotted a man who was sitting with a blue book. He was reading quietly, but something about him made me keep watching. Then he looked at me. He stared. He stood up suddenly, spilling his coffee. Why did he get up so quickly? Where was he going? I stirred my coffee and took a last sip. Then I got up and followed him.

Pages 88–89: Find the Hidden Treasure
The treasure is at D2.

Page 92: Monster Crossword

1 c	2 l	a	3 w	s				4 g
	u		h					r
	m		i					e
	p		5 s	q	u	a	r	e
	y		k					n
			6 e	i	g	h	t	
			r					
			7 s	n	o	8 u	t	
						g		
		9 c	i	r	c	l	e	s
						y		

Page 93: Alien Anagrams
a – 3, b – 8, c – 4, d – 11, e – 5, f – 10, g – 1, h – 6, i – 12, j – 7, k – 2, l – 9

6-7 years

Leap Ahead

BUMPER Workbook

Key Stage 1

MATHS

Home learning made **FUN!**

Numbers to 100

Dexter and Jason are at the cinema. Match the ticket numbers with the correct seats.

sixty-three
forty-two
thirty-one
twenty-three

17

23

seventy-five
forty-eight
seventeen
thirty-six

28

82

31

sixty-seven
twenty-eight
fifty-nine
eighty-two

75

36

67

42

48

59

63

Find the correct number sticker to match these number words.

thirty-five

fifty-two

eighty-one

twenty-four

Answers on page 128

Place Value

These cinema tickets have been ripped up. Draw a line to match the 'ten' and 'one' part needed to make each of the numbers below. One has been done for you.

~~23~~ 78 52 36 85 41 94 67

60 4 50 5

40 8 90 3

30 7 20 6

80 2 70 1

Answers on page 128

Write three different numbers using the tens and ones below. Try to write the word versions too. One has been done for you.

30, 40 5, 8

45 forty-five

PARENT TIP: Make 2 sets of numbers cards, multiples of 10 up to 90 and single digits 0 to 9. Pick one card from each set and ask your child to say and write the number, e.g. 40 and 2 makes 42. Knowing that 42 is made of 40 + 2 is critical for later work on calculations.

Counting Large Numbers

Harry and Amelia are counting their marbles. Each bag contains 10 marbles. Including the marbles on the ground, how many marbles in total does each child have?

Steve's box of bricks has fallen over! Circle the pieces in groups of 5. Now count in 5s to find the total. Write the total in the box.

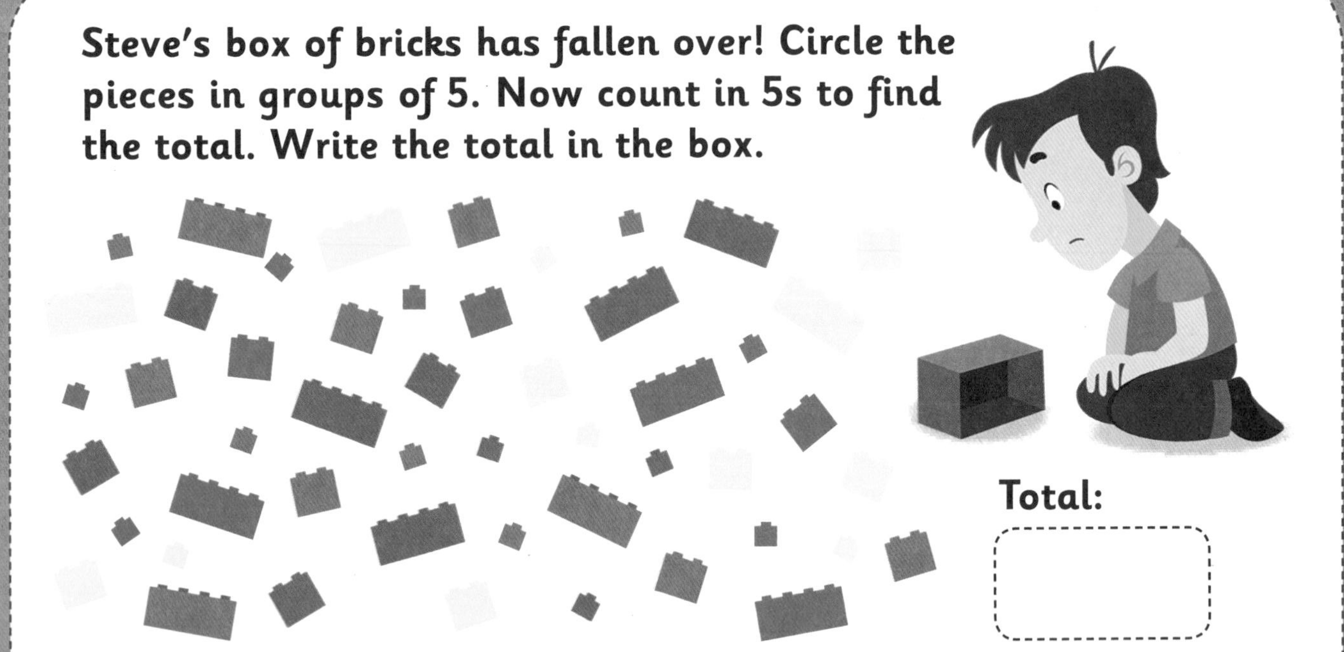

Complete the sequence using number stickers to fill the gaps.

5, 10, 15, 20, ☐, ☐, 35, ☐, 45

Answers on page 128

Jack and Sam have been playing with their cars. They have made a traffic jam! How many cars are there altogether? Count in 2s to find out.

[ ] cars altogether

Steve, Matt and Mike have saved all their pocket money. Count in 2s, 5s and 10s to work out how much they each have.

Steve = [ ] p   Matt = [ ] p   Mike = [ ] p

Who has the most? ______________________________

Answers on page 128

PARENT TIP: Children need to move away from counting all objects one by one and use their skills of counting in 2s, 5s and 10s. Tip some pasta shells onto the table and count how many there are by first grouping them into 2s, 5s or 10s, then counting in those steps.

Make 10, 20 and 100

Amy, Joshua and Philip are helping out at the supermarket. Joshua must collect pairs of bags that together contain 10 oranges. Join pairs that make 10.

Complete these missing number puzzles.

1 + ☐ = 10 7 + ☐ = 10 10 = 4 + ☐

☐ + 5 = 10 ☐ + 8 = 10 6 + 4 = ☐

Answers on page 128

PARENT TIP: Play Speedy Pairs. One person calls out a number from 0 to 9. Two players compete to say the bond to ten as quickly as they can, e.g. if 4 is said, the bond to 10 is 6. Instant recall of bonds to 10 is very helpful in later calculation work.

Amy is filling bags with 20 tomatoes. How many more must she add to each bag to make 20?

Philip is sorting out a special offer on collector's cards. He needs to find 2 packets that contain 100 cards altogether. Which should he choose? Circle them.

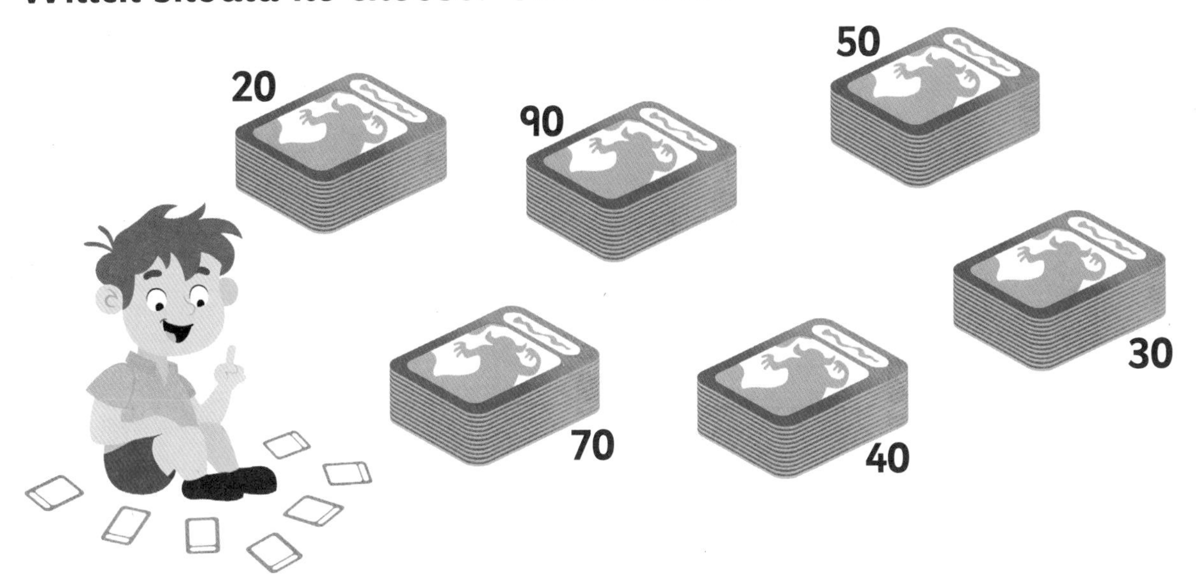

Complete the calculations below. One has been done for you.

20 + 80 = 100

30 + ☐ = 100

☐ + 60 = 100

50 + ☐ = 100

80 + ☐ = 100

90 + ☐ = 100

Answers on page 128

Line Symmetry

Josie loves to play shape games on her tablet. In this game, she must draw a line of symmetry on each shape. Can you help?

Answers on page 128

A line of symmetry cuts a shape into 2 halves. When the shape is folded along the line of symmetry, the 2 halves sit on top of each other.

Cross out the shapes below that have lines of symmetry drawn in the wrong position.

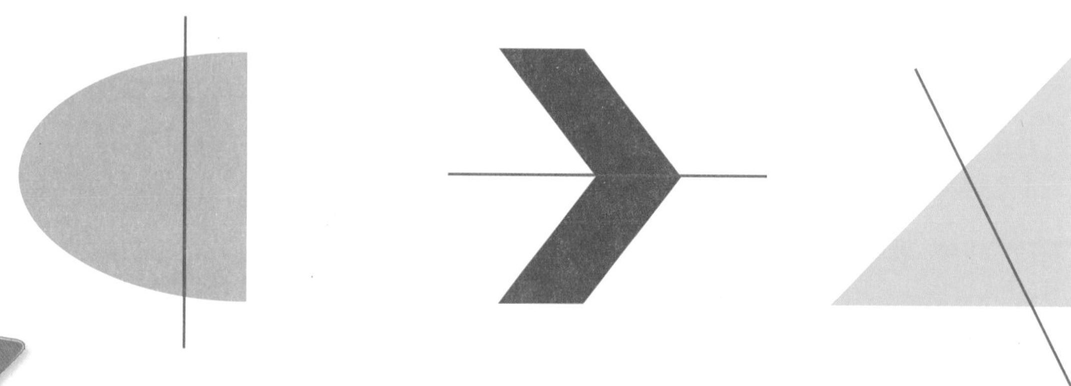

Draw the other halves of these symmetrical pictures.

Complete this picture then colour it in, but make sure the picture stays symmetrical.

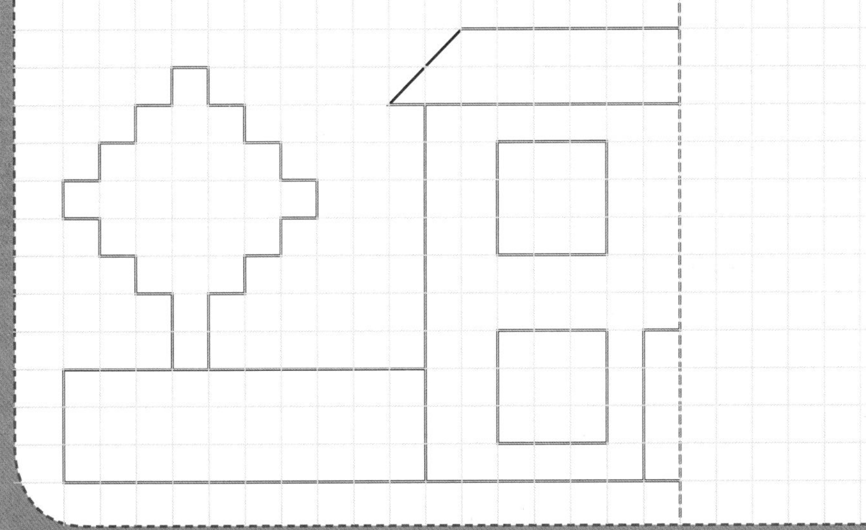

PARENT TIP: Children can confuse reflective symmetry with work on fractions and halving. Although the line of symmetry cuts the image in half, one half must be a reflection of the other. Holding a mirror along the line of symmetry can help to see what the reflected 'half' should look like. Folding shapes in half also helps the child to check the symmetry.

Money Maths

Jess and Archie have come to the sweet shop. They each have 50p pocket money to spend.

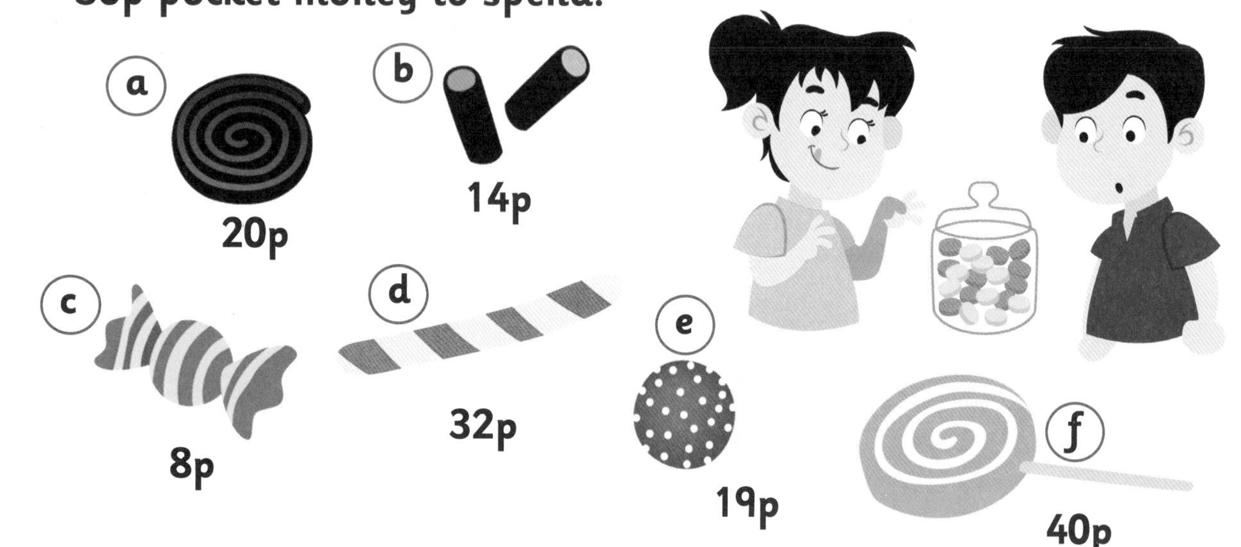

Jess buys a and e.

Cost: 20p + 19p = ☐ Change: 50p - ☐ = ☐

Archie buys f and c.

Cost: 40p + 8p = ☐ Change: 50p - ☐ = ☐

What would you choose to buy? Find out the cost and the change you would get from 50p.

Working out and answer space

Is it possible to buy 3 sweets for less than 50p? ☐

Answers on page 128

PARENT TIP: Look for opportunities to buy small things in shops with coins rather than credit cards. Count up to find change, e.g. if an item costs 68p and £1 is paid, count up in ones from 68p to 70p, then count up in tens to £1 to calculate the change. Children need lots of practice with this in real shops or during pretend play.

The sweet shop also sells boxes of chocolate. Put chocolate box stickers against each price. Which box do you think should cost the most?

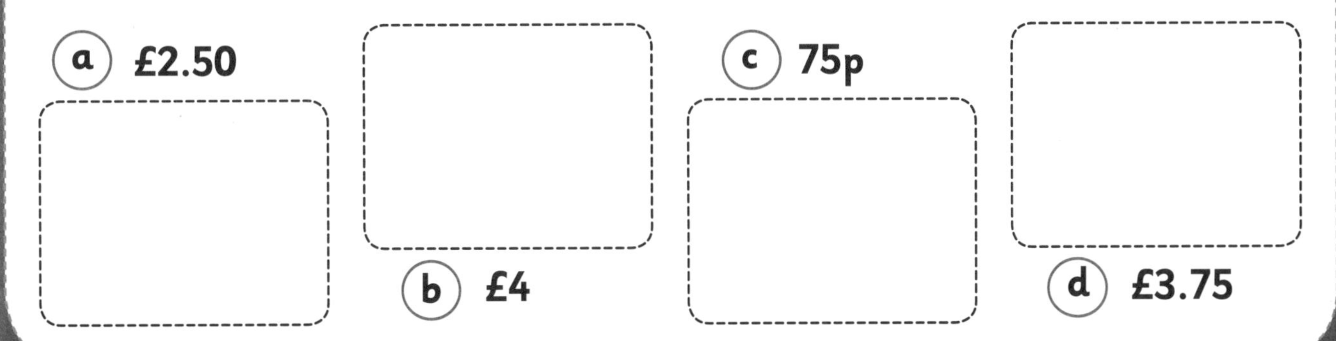

Darren is choosing a box of chocolates for his mum's birthday. Work out the change from £5 that Darren would get if he bought each box of chocolates.

Box a - £2 and 50p Change from £5 =

Box b - £4 Change from £5 =

Box c - 75p Change from £5 =

Box d - £3 and 75p Change from £5 =

Jack has bought a mystery gift for his dad. He paid £1 and was given 35p change. Which gift did he buy?

Answers on page 128

2D Shapes

Class 2 have entered a swimming competition.
Their teacher is sorting out the badges for the winners.

The badges are pentagon, hexagon and octagon shaped.

pentagons

hexagons

octagons

Find the swimming badge stickers and put them in the correct boxes.

pentagon	hexagon	octagon

Name and draw a 3-sided shape.

Name and draw a 4-sided shape.

Count the sides and corners on these regular shapes and complete the chart.

What do you notice?

....

....

....

....

Does this work for irregular shapes too? Test it out.

Regular shape name	Number of sides	Number of corners
Triangle		
Square		
Pentagon		
Hexagon		
Octagon		

These children have won swimming badges. Count the number of pentagon, hexagon and octagon badges.

☐ **Pentagons**

☐ **Hexagons**

☐ **Octagons**

Answers on page 128

PARENT TIP: Play Guess My Shape. Think of a 2D shape but keep it secret. Your child asks questions about the properties of the shape in a bid to guess it. You must only answer yes or no. Take turns and try to guess the shapes, asking the fewest questions.

Compare and Order Numbers

Adam had a bowling party for his birthday and invited 5 friends. Here are their final scores for game 1.

Adam	Ben	Chloe	David	Ellie	Frankie
76	45	62	58	81	73

Who won? ______________________

Put their names and scores in order from highest to lowest, using the stickers for game 1 on the sticker sheet.

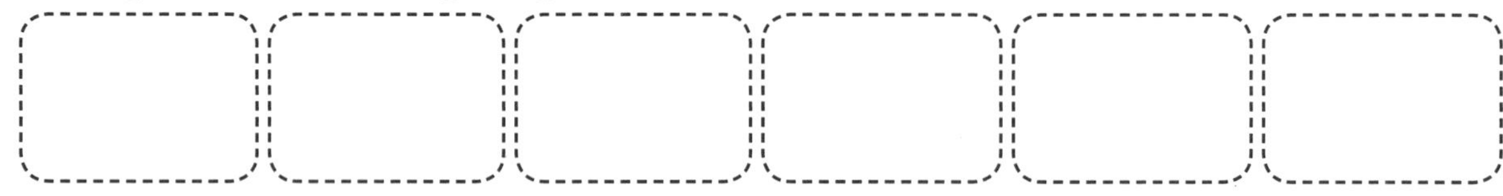

Find the final scores for game 2 on the sticker sheet.
Put them in order here, this time from lowest to highest.

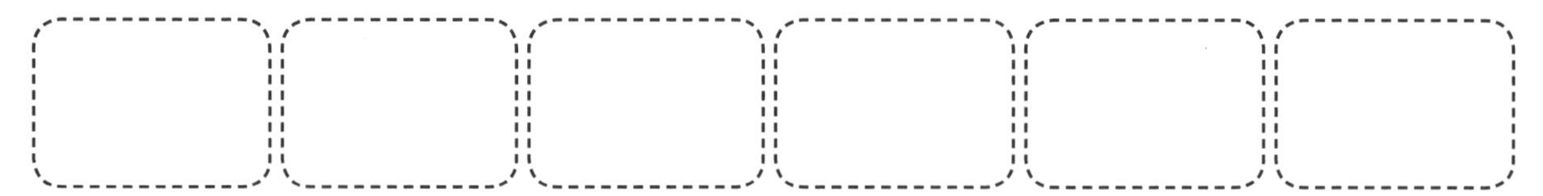

Who had the lowest score? ______________________

Put the scores from the other lanes in order too, from smallest to largest. One has been done for you.

Lane 1:
75 43 29 84 53 25

Lane 2:
98 37 16 55 39 42

Lane 3:
26 84 38 67 53 62

Answers on page 128

Make six 2-digit numbers of your own. Choose one 'ten' number and one single digit number and combine to make your 2-digit numbers. Write the numbers in a list in the box to the right.

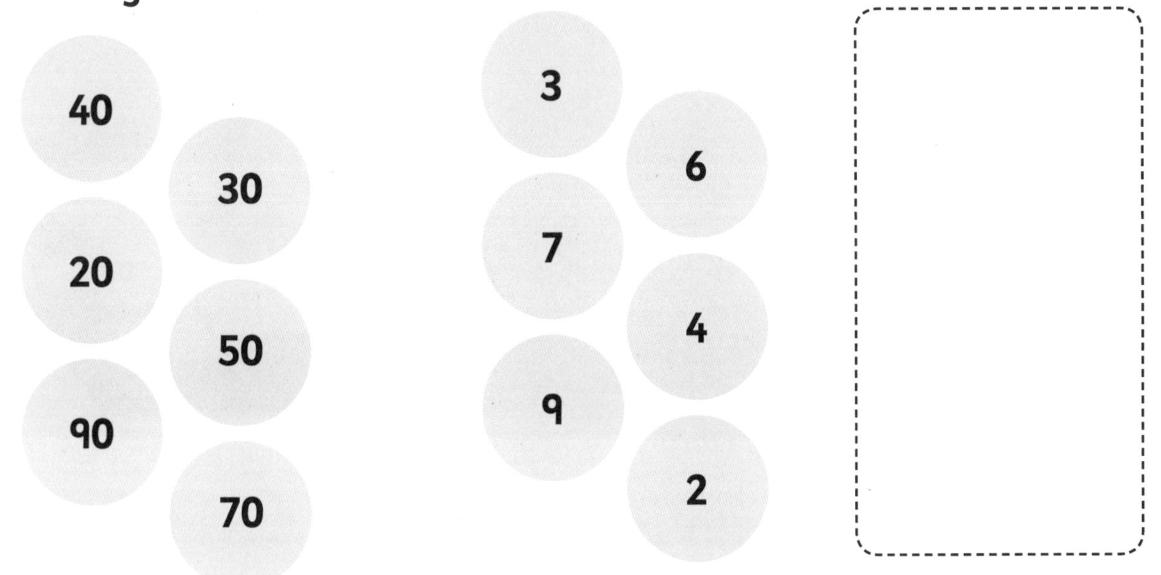

Now put your numbers in order from largest to smallest.

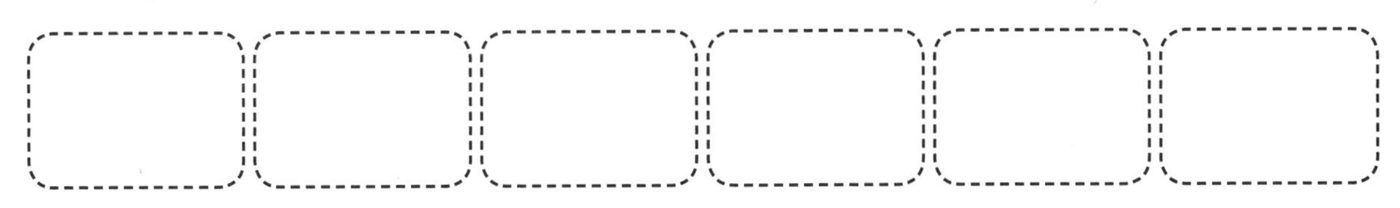

Use inequality signs to compare these pairs of numbers.

58 ☐ 72	26 ☐ 20	37 ☐ 28
81 ☐ 63	49 ☐ 32	65 ☐ 84

< less than **> more than**

Answers on page 128

PARENT TIP: When ordering numbers, encourage your child to compare the 'tens' digits first and then the 'ones' digits if necessary. A useful image for remembering the inequality signs is to imagine them as a crocodile's mouth. Remind your child that "the crocodile always eats the larger number".

Adding Numbers

Year 2 are working hard at school, adding numbers.
Help Conrad's group to complete these length calculations.

20cm + 7cm =

45cm + 2cm =

62cm + 3cm =

31cm + 7cm =

38cm + 10cm =

57cm + 20cm =

43cm + 30cm =

Jessica's group has been rolling three 9-sided dice and writing down the results. Find the totals.

3 + 5 + 2 =

4 + 6 + 3 =

8 + 3 + 5 =

2 + 1 + 4 =

7 + 3 + 5 =

7 + 4 + 9 =

Answers on page 128

Ruby's group use a 100 square to add 32 + 24. First they find 32 on the grid and circle it. Then, they add 24 by counting on 2 tens and 4 ones. Finally, they finish on the answer, 56.

1	2	3	4	5	6	7	8	9	10
11	12	13	14	15	16	17	18	19	20
21	22	23	24	25	26	27	28	29	30
31	32	33	34	35	36	37	38	39	40
41	42	43	44	45	46	47	48	49	50
51	52	53	54	55	56	57	58	59	60
61	62	63	64	65	66	67	68	69	70
71	72	73	74	75	76	77	78	79	80
81	82	83	84	85	86	87	88	89	90
91	92	93	94	95	96	97	98	99	100

Use the 100 grid to solve these additions.

1. 16 + 23 = ☐
2. 45 + 23 = ☐
3. 31 + 47 = ☐
4. 63 + 36 = ☐
5. 25 + ☐ = 54
6. 18 + ☐ = 59

Now collect a 'well done' sticker and put it here on your work.

Answers on page 128

PARENT TIP: Play Dice Totals. Take turns to roll 3 dice, writing down the numbers rolled. Add them up to find the totals. The highest total wins the round. Another version is to roll 2 dice, letting one represent 'tens' and one represent 'ones'. Combine to create a 2-digit number, e.g. roll 4 and 3 make 43. The largest number wins the round.

Measures

It is Sports Day at school. Class 1 have completed the long jump. Measure each jump in centimetres using a ruler.

Multiply each jump measurement by 10 to get the real measurement.

Jump	Picture measurement	Actual measurement (x10)
1	6cm	60cm
2		
3		
4		
5		

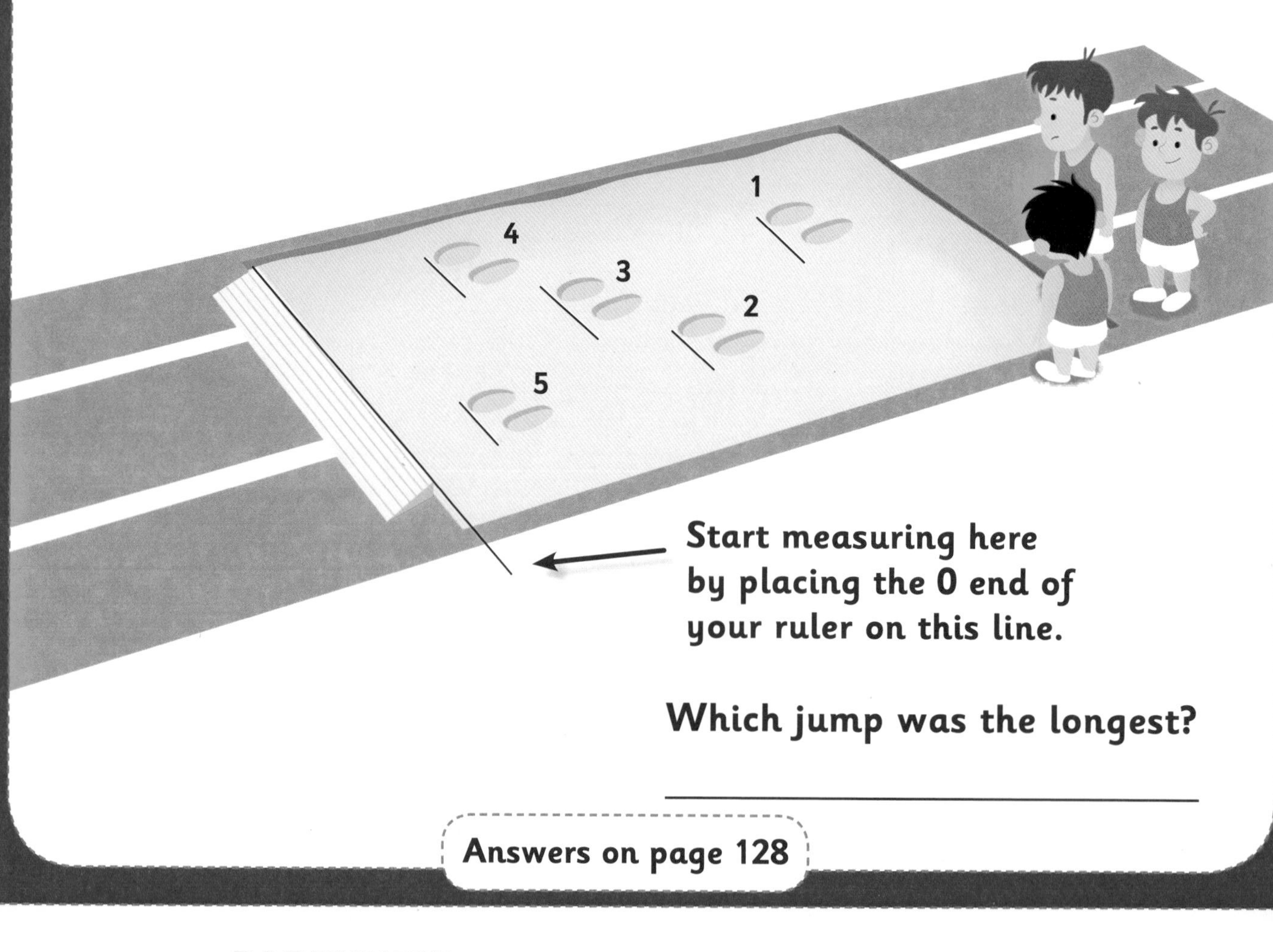

Start measuring here by placing the 0 end of your ruler on this line.

Which jump was the longest?

____

Answers on page 128

PARENT TIP: Take turns to do long jumps at home. Mark the start and end points and use a tape measure to measure the lengths in metres and centimetres. Who can jump the furthest? Order the jumps by their lengths from shortest to longest.

Class 2 did some weight lifting. These are the weights they lifted. Write how heavy they were to the nearest kilogram.

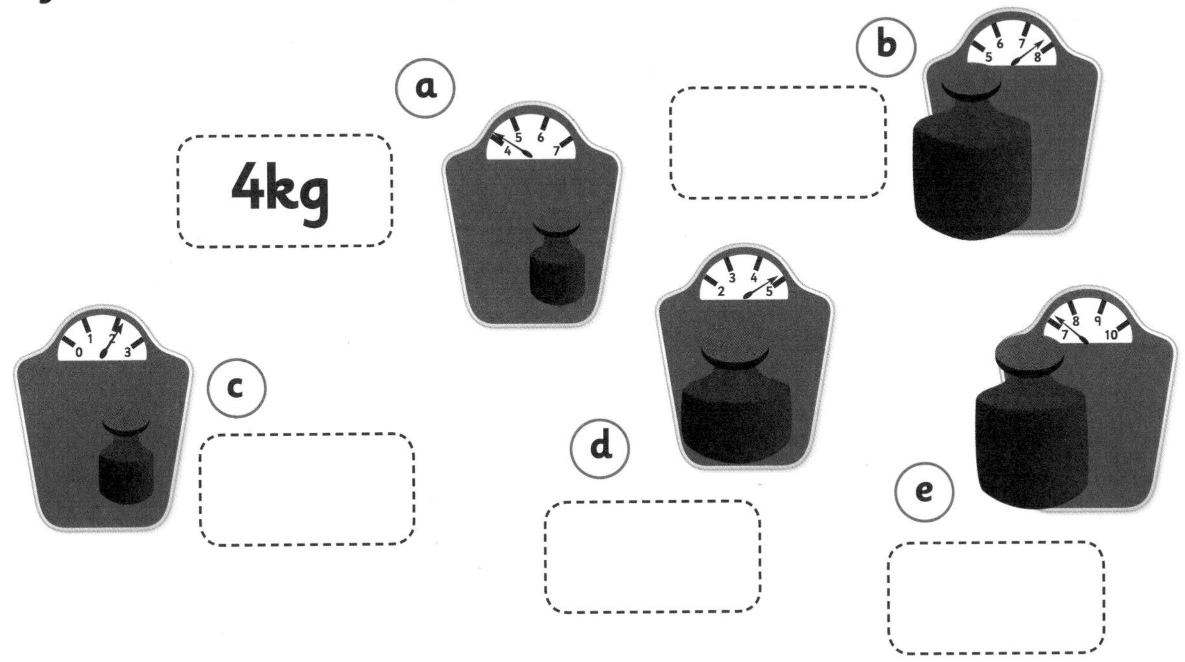

Mrs Brown prepared some drinks for the children. Colour each jug to show the correct measurement.

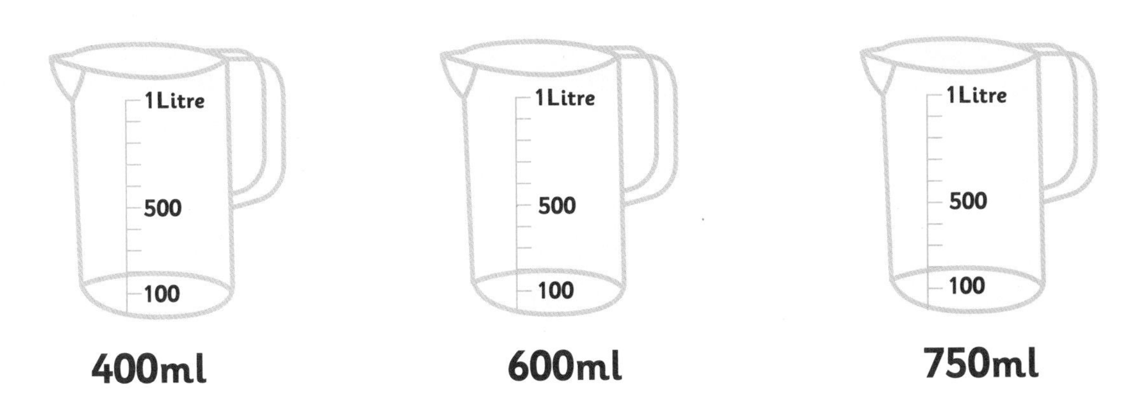

Find the jug stickers and put them in order by the volume they contain, from smallest to largest.

Answers on page 128

Subtracting Numbers

Lottie is stuck with these subtractions. Can you help her?

54 – 4 =

32 – 2 =

29 – 9 =

74 – 30 =

58 – 20 =

65 – 40 =

Her teacher uses a 100 grid to show how to count back in 'tens' and 'ones' for subtraction, e.g. 48 - 23 = 25.

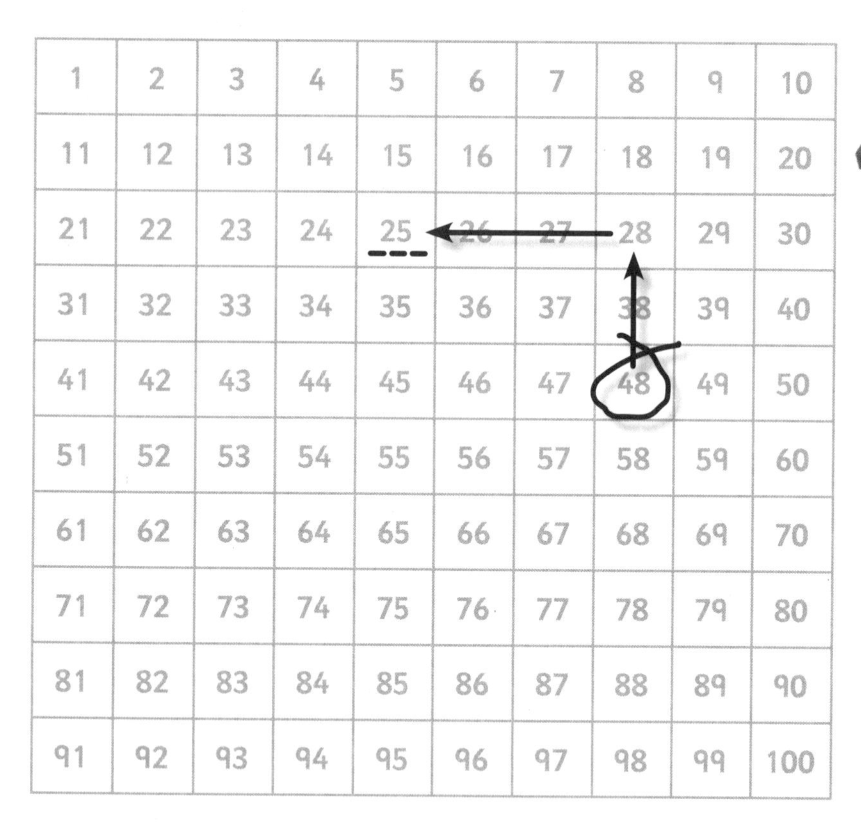

1	2	3	4	5	6	7	8	9	10
11	12	13	14	15	16	17	18	19	20
21	22	23	24	25	26	27	28	29	30
31	32	33	34	35	36	37	38	39	40
41	42	43	44	45	46	47	48	49	50
51	52	53	54	55	56	57	58	59	60
61	62	63	64	65	66	67	68	69	70
71	72	73	74	75	76	77	78	79	80
81	82	83	84	85	86	87	88	89	90
91	92	93	94	95	96	97	98	99	100

Complete these subtraction calculations.

Use the 100 grid to help you.

75 – 24 =

63 – 41 =

49 – 27 =

89 – 64 =

Answers on page 128

Mr Potter keeps track of the house points each class has earned. Find the difference between last week's scores and this week's scores for each class (count up from the smaller number to the larger number).

Class	Last week	This week	Difference
1	63	58	
2	71	67	
3	48	52	
4	79	83	
5	62	56	

Join each subtraction calculation to its answer.

26 – 12

78 – 24

56 – 32

21

16

14

54

23

24

35 – 14

47 – 31

69 – 46

Now collect a 'well done' sticker from the sticker sheet and put it in this box.

Answers on page 128

PARENT TIP: Play snakes and ladders in reverse. Start at 100 and take turns to roll 2 dice, so you can create a 2-digit number, e.g. a 2 and a 3 gives you 23. Count back towards zero to find the winner.

Multiplying by 2, 5 and 10

Carly is counting on the number grid. She starts at 2 and counts on in 2s. Colour the numbers she lands on in red. Then she starts at 5 and counts on in 5s. Colour the numbers she lands on in blue.

1	2	3	4	5	6	7	8	9	10
11	12	13	14	15	16	17	18	19	20
21	22	23	24	25	26	27	28	29	30
31	32	33	34	35	36	37	38	39	40
41	42	43	44	45	46	47	48	49	50

Did you colour some numbers twice?
Write those numbers here:

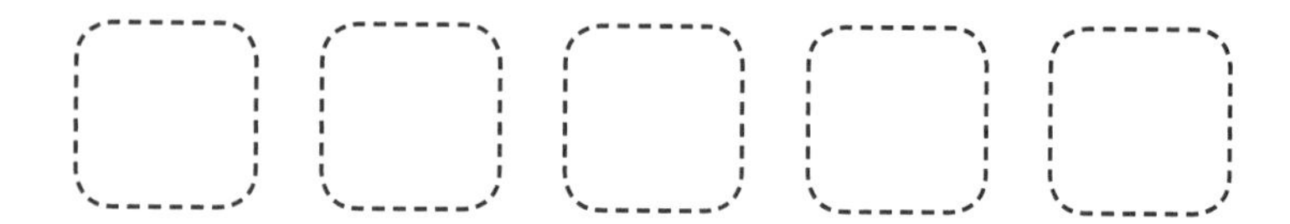

What can you say about these numbers?

Help Dylan complete the number sequences. Choose number stickers from the sticker sheet to fill the empty boxes.

4 - ___ - 8 - 10 - ___ - ___ - 16 - ___

5 - 10 - ___ - 20 - ___ - 30 - ___ - ___

80 - 70 - ___ - ___ - 40 - ___ - 20 - ___

Answers on page 128

Jasper is organising a party for his friends.
How many are there of each food item?

3 plates of 2 pizzas

pizzas

$3 \times 2 =$ ☐

6 bunches of 5 grapes

grapes

$6 \times 5 =$ ☐

4 trays of 2 cakes

cakes

$4 \times 2 =$ ☐

2 baskets of 5 bread rolls

bread rolls

$2 \times 5 =$ ☐

7 packets of 2 drink cartons

drink cartons

$7 \times 2 =$ ☐

3 plates of 5 sandwiches

sandwiches

$3 \times 5 =$ ☐

Answers on page 128

PARENT TIP: Look for food items at home that come in multiple packets. Give your child some problems to solve, e.g. There are 6 cakes in each box, how many in 2 boxes? There are 8 apples in each bag, how many in 5 bags?

Block Graphs and Tallies

The theme park staff keep a record of the rides people go on. Answer the questions using the information in the block graph to help.

1 block = 5 riders

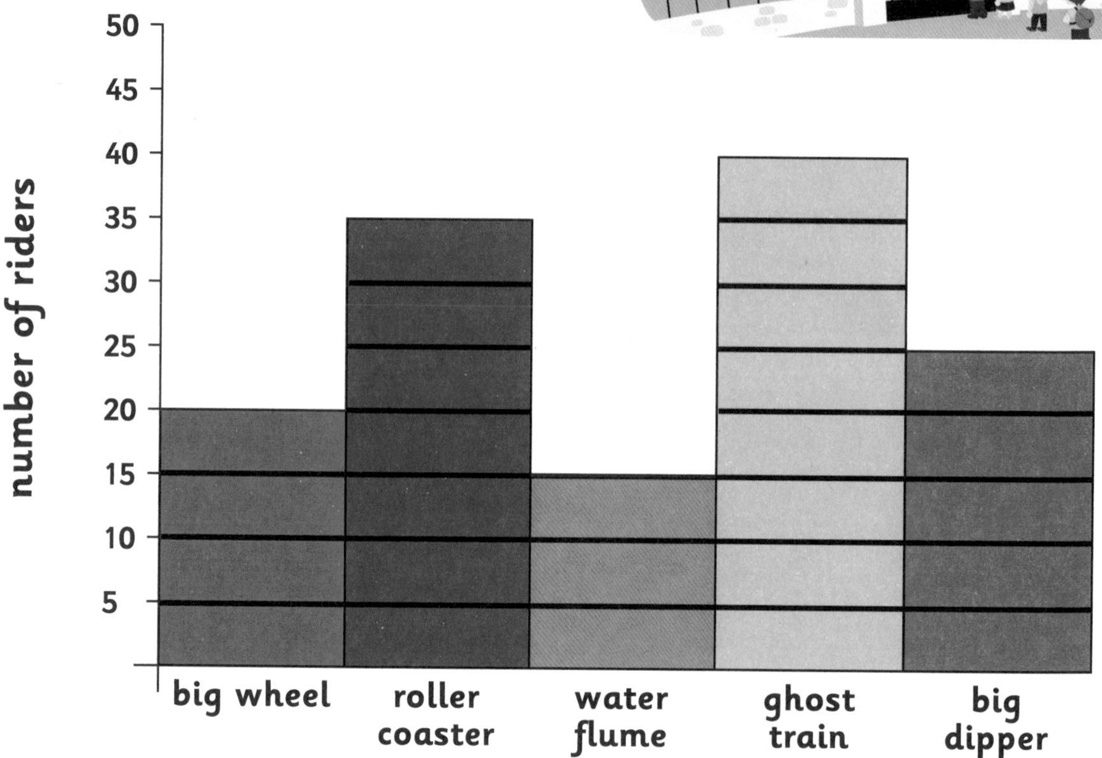

Which ride was used most? ____________________

Which ride was used 40 times? ____________________

How many more riders went on the roller coaster than the big dipper?

How many riders used the big wheel?

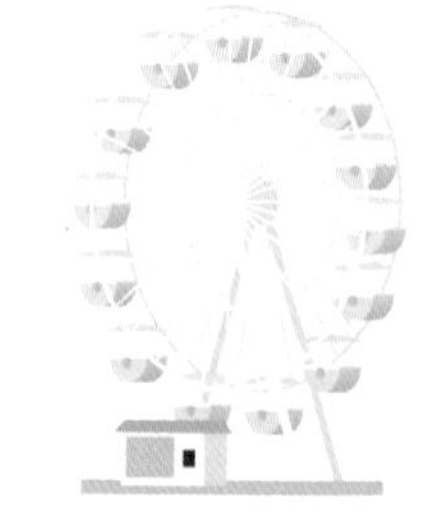

You and four friends go to the theme park. Choose your two favourite rides and add your information to the block graph using the block stickers on the sticker sheet.

Answers on page 128

The toddler section has smaller rides for young children. The staff have kept a tally of the number of riders. Complete the total riders column below.

Ride	Tally	Total riders
Slide	~~1111~~ 111	
Bouncy castle	~~1111~~ ~~1111~~ 11	
Teacups	11	
Roundabout	~~1111~~ 1	

Put the information into this block graph by colouring blocks.
1 block = 2 riders

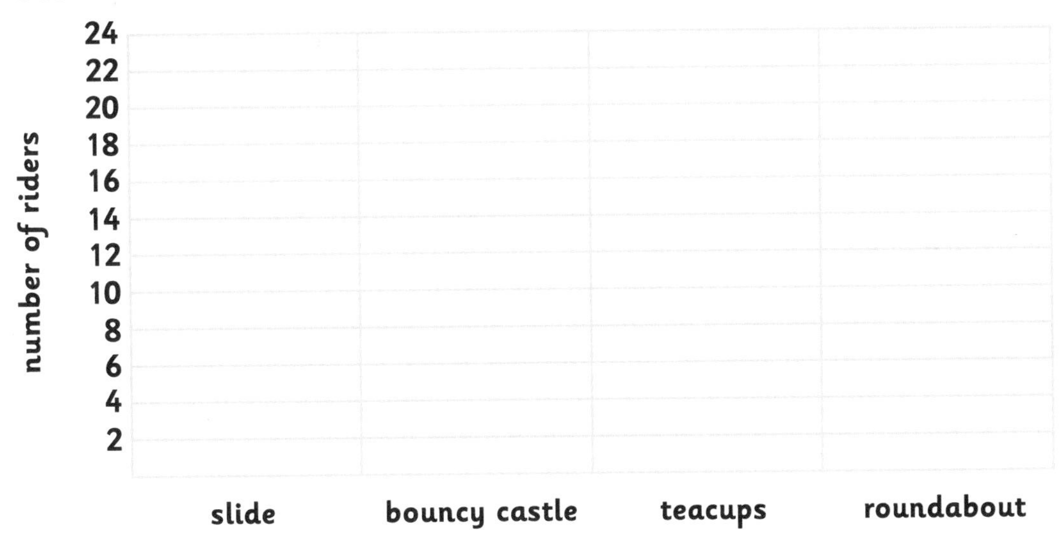

Which ride was used most? ______________________

How many children used the teacups and the roundabout? [ ]

Which ride had 8 riders? ______________________

Answers on page 128

PARENT TIP: Collect information from family and friends about their favourite foods, colours, pets or TV programmes and use tallies to record the results. Then construct a block graph to display the information collected. What does it tell you?

Dividing

Becky and Jack are at football training. The coach needs 5 groups for the warm-up activity. How many children should be in each group? Split the children into 5 groups, circling each group.

Each group needs 2 balls. Put ball stickers in the group boxes. How many balls are needed altogether?

After the warm-up activity, the players are allowed to share some orange segments.

There are 5 groups of players.
How many orange segments can each group have?

Answers on page 128

Fractions

Here are the football team's socks.
Colour $\frac{1}{2}$ of them red, $\frac{1}{4}$ of them green and $\frac{1}{4}$ of them yellow.

$\frac{1}{2}$ of 20 = ☐ $\frac{1}{4}$ of 20 = ☐

Colour the correct fraction on the team flags.

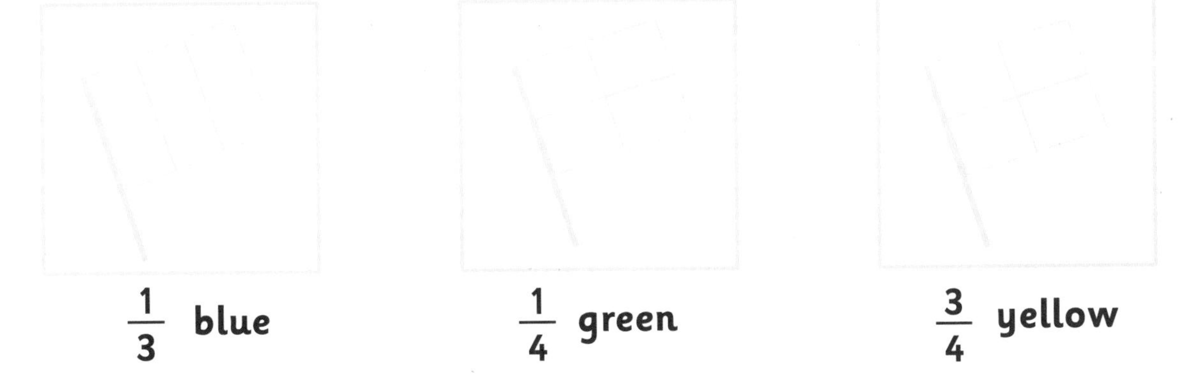

$\frac{1}{3}$ blue $\frac{1}{4}$ green $\frac{3}{4}$ yellow

Answers on page 128

PARENT TIP: Children need to remember that the denominator of the fraction (number at bottom) tells us how many equal parts the object or number is split into. The numerator of the fraction (number at top) tells us how many of those parts to colour or count.

3D Shapes and Patterns

Describe the faces of each shape so Gill can guess what they are.

2 squares

4 rectangles

....

....

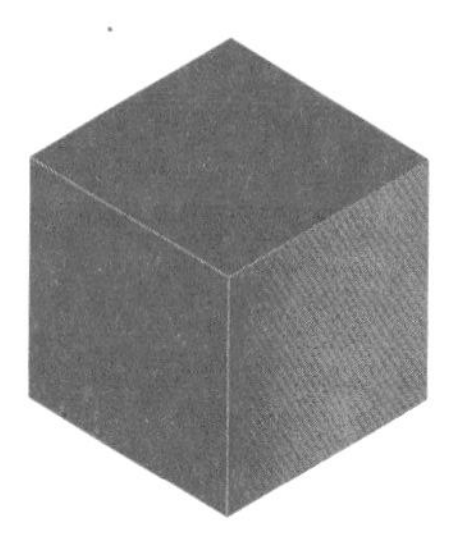

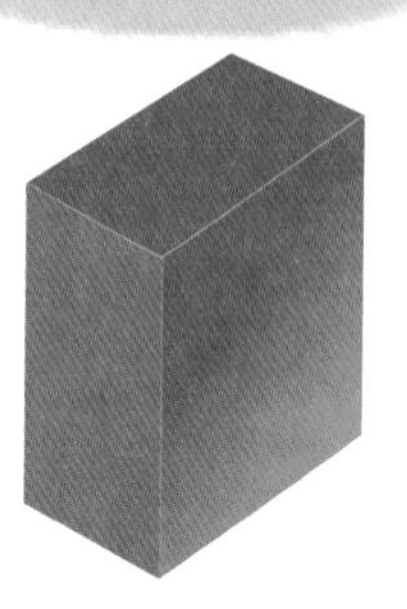

....

....

Jeremy has found some 3D shapes with curved faces. Name the shapes and count the corners on each.

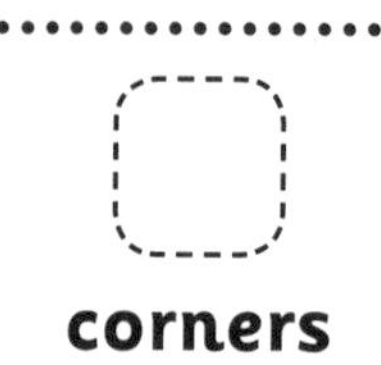

....

corners corners corners

Answers on page 128

Use stickers from the sticker sheet to help Charlie complete the shape patterns.

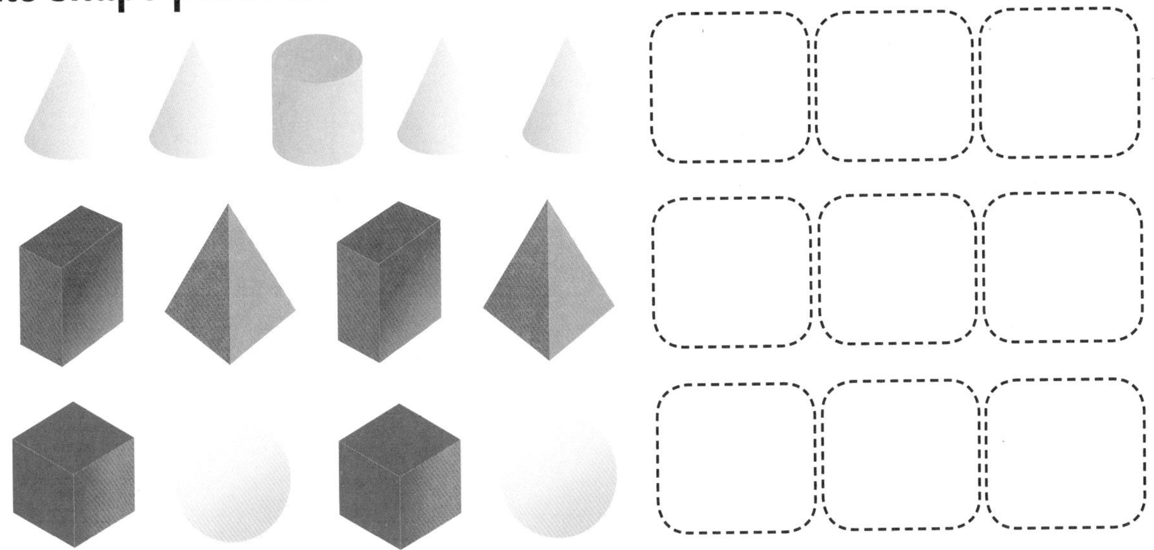

This beautiful butterfly is missing some of its pattern. Use stickers to make both sides look the same. It must be symmetrical.

PARENT TIP: Play Describe And Copy games. Player 1 makes a pattern or shape from bricks. Player 2 cannot see, but has a pile of similar bricks. Player 1 then describes their pattern and shape to Player 2 who tries to build a matching pattern and shape. Reveal both creations and see if the two match.

Telling the Time

Johnny needs to catch a bus to visit his grandma. The bus times for each day are below.

Monday

Tuesday

Wednesday

Thursday

Friday

It is Thursday today. What time does the bus leave? ________

The journey back home takes an hour. When will Johnny arrive?

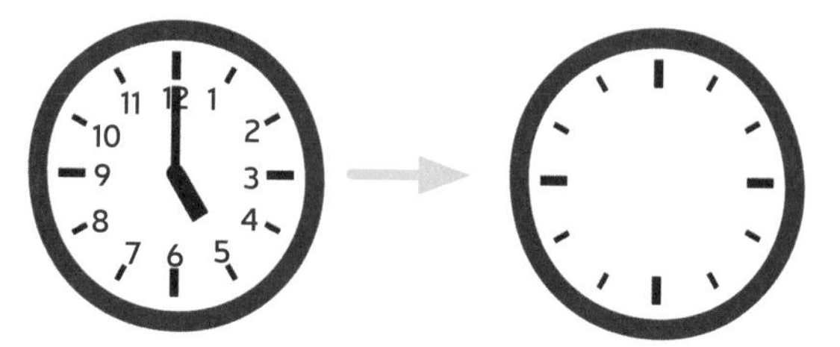

Find the correct clock stickers to show these times:

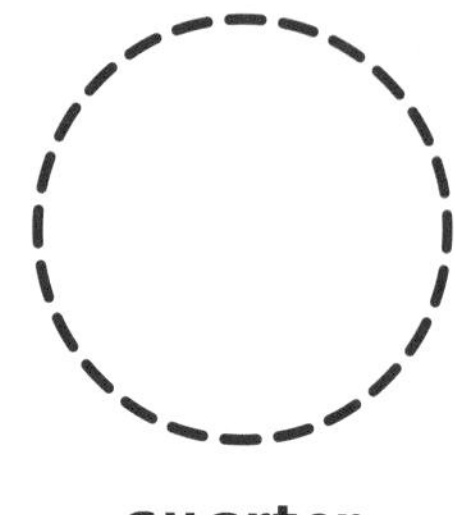

quarter past 8

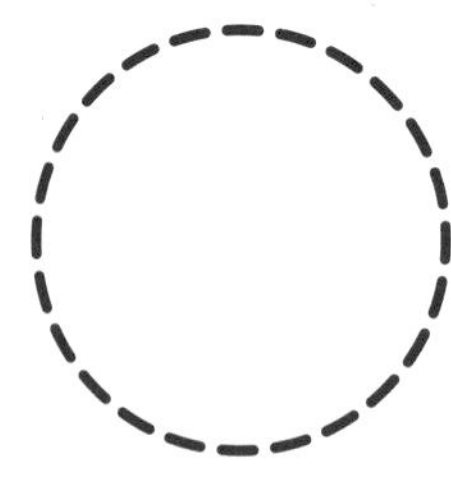

half past 2

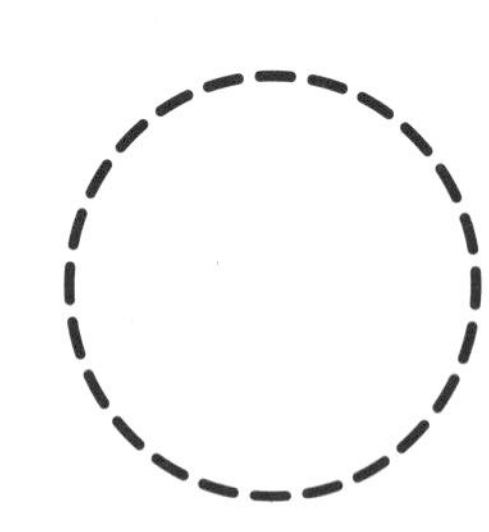

quarter to 5

Write the times shown on these clocks:

------------- ------------- -------------

Answers on page 128

PARENT TIP: Telling the time needs lots of practice. Give your child a watch and regularly ask them o'clock, half past and quarter to and past times. Remind them the long hand tells them the minutes past and the short hand tells them the hour. Plan to do things at a given time and keep checking when that time comes.

Puzzles

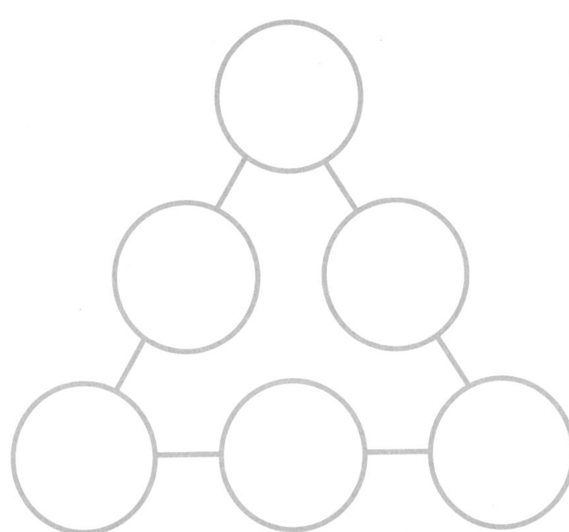

Use the numbers 1, 2, 3, 4, 5, 6. Write them on the triangle so that each side adds up to 10. Can you do it another way, too?

I think of a number and then double it. The answer is 8. What was my number?

I think of a number and then subtract 6. The answer is 14. What was my number?

This is a magic square. Every row, column and diagonal adds up to 15. Can you complete it? Use the numbers 1–9 only once.

4		
	5	
		6

Answers on page 128

Page 98: Numbers to 100
35 - thirty-five 52 - fifty-two 81 - eighty-one 24 - twenty-four

Page 99: Place Value

23 78 52 36 85 41 94 67

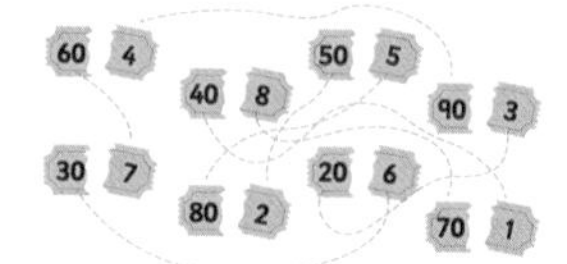

Page 100: Counting Large Numbers
Harry has 28 marbles.
Amelia has 32 marbles.
Steve has a total of 50 bricks.
5, 10, 15, 20, **25**, **30**, 35, **40**, 45

Page 101: Counting Large Numbers (continued)
Jack and Sam have 16 cars altogether.
Steve = 18p / Matt = 45p / Mike = 90p
Mike has the most money.

Page 102: Make 10, 20 and 100
1 + 9 = 10, 7 + 3 = 10, 10 = 4 + 6, 5 + 5 = 10,
2 + 8 = 10, 6 + 4 = 10

Page 103: Make 10, 20 and 100 (continued)
14 + 6 = 20, 12 + 8 = 20, 17 + 3 = 20, 16 + 4 = 20,
13 + 7 = 20, 19 + 1 = 20
Philip should choose the pack of 70 and the pack of 30.
20 + 80 = 100, 30 + 70 = 100, 40 + 60 = 100
50 + 50 = 100, 80 + 20 = 100, 90 + 10 = 100

Page 104: Line Symmetry
Answers could include:

Page 106: Money Maths
Jess: 20p + 19p = 39p Change: 50p - 39p = 11p
Archie: 40p + 8p = 48p Change: 50p - 48p = 2p
It is possible to buy 3 sweets for less than 50p.

Page 107: Money Maths (continued)
Box a change: £2.50, Box b change: £1.00, Box c change: £4.25, Box d change: £1.25. Jack bought gift b.

Page 109: 2D Shapes

1 Pentagon
2 Hexagons
3 Octagons

Regular shape name	Number of sides	Number of corners
Triangle	3	3
Square	4	4
Pentagon	5	5
Hexagon	6	6
Octagon	8	8

Page 110: Compare and Order Numbers
game 1: Ellie 81, Adam 76, Frankie 73, Chloe 62, David 58, Ben 45
game 2: Ellie 35, Chloe 42, David 50, Adam 77, Ben 79, Frankie 93
Lane 1: 25, 29, 43, 53, 75, 84
Lane 2: 16, 37, 39, 42, 55, 98
Lane 3: 26, 38, 53, 62, 67, 84

Page 111: Compare and Order Numbers (continued)
58 < 72 26 > 20 37 > 28 81 > 63 49 > 32 65 < 84

Page 112: Adding Numbers
20cm + 7cm = 27cm, 45cm + 2cm = 47cm,
38cm + 10cm = 48cm, 45cm + 2cm = 47cm,
62cm + 3cm = 65cm, 31cm + 7cm = 38cm,
38cm + 10cm = 48cm, 57cm + 20cm = 77cm,
43cm + 30cm = 73cm
3 + 5 + 2 = 10, 2 + 1 + 4 = 7, 4 + 6 + 3 = 13,
7 + 3 + 5 = 15, 8 + 3 + 5 = 16, 7 + 4 + 9 = 20

Page 113: Adding Numbers (continued)
16 + 23 = 39, 45 + 23 = 68, 31 + 47 = 78, 63 + 36 = 99,
25 + 29 = 54, 18 + 41 = 59

Page 114: Measures

Jump 1 is the longest.

Jump	Picture measurement	Actual measurement (x10)
1	6cm	60cm
2	4cm	40cm
3	3cm	30cm
4	2cm	20cm
5	1cm	10cm

Page 115: Measures (continued)
a: 4kg b: 8kg c: 2kg d: 5kg e: 7kg

Page 116: Subtracting Numbers
54 - 4 = 50, 32 - 2 = 30, 29 - 9 = 20, 74 - 30 = 44, 58 - 20 = 38,
65 - 40 = 25, 75 - 24 = 51, 63 - 41 = 22, 49 - 27 = 22, 89 - 64 = 25

Page 117: Subtracting Numbers (continued)

Class	Last week	This week	Difference
1	63	58	5
2	71	67	4
3	48	52	4
4	79	83	4
5	62	56	6

26 - 12 = 14 78 - 24 = 54 56 - 32 = 24 35 - 14 = 21 47 - 31 = 16 69 - 46 = 23

Page 118: Multiplying by 2, 5 and 10
4 - 6 - 8 - 10 - 12 - 14 - 16 - 18 5 - 10 - 15 - 20 - 25 - 30 - 35 - 40
80 - 70 - 60 - 50 - 40 - 30 - 20 - 10

Page 119: Multiplying by 2, 5 and 10 (continued)
6 pizzas, 30 grapes, 8 cakes, 10 bread rolls, 14 drink cartons, 15 sandwiches

Page 120: Block Graphs and Tallies
The ghost train was used the most. The ghost train was used 40 times.
10 more riders on the roller coaster. 20 riders used the big wheel.

Page 121: Block Graphs and Tallies (continued)
slide = 8 riders, bouncy castle = 12 riders, teacups = 2 riders,
roundabout = 6 riders. The bouncy castle was used the most.
8 riders used the teacups and the roundabout. The slide had 8 riders.

Page 122: Dividing
There are 3 children in each group, 10 balls are needed altogether.
Each group will have 6 segments of orange.

Page 123: Fractions
$\frac{1}{2}$ of 20 = 10 $\frac{1}{4}$ of 20 = 5

Page 124: 3D Shapes and Patterns
cylinder: 0 corners, cone: 1 corner, sphere: 0 corners

Page 126: Telling the Time
The bus leaves at 8:00 (8 o'clock).

1. 10:05 2. 7:20 3. 10:50

Page 127: Puzzles
starting number = 4
starting number = 20

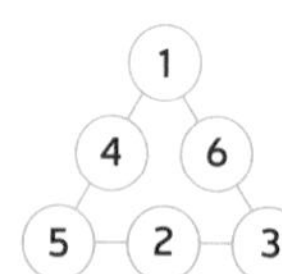

4	9	2
3	5	7
8	1	6